Sixteen immortal characteristic inter
by Albert W. Ketèlbey

Ketèlbey Classics *fo*

Selected & edited with
an Introduction by Tom McCanna

Bosworth

Cover designed by Michael Bell Design.
Music Setting by Enigma Music Production Services.

Order No. BOE005031
ISMN: M-2016-4040-2
ISBN: 978-1-84938-697-5

Head Office:
14-15 Berners Street, London W1T 3LJ, UK.
Telephone: +44 (0)20 7612 7400.
Fax: +44 (0)20 7612 7545.

Sales & Hire:
Music Sales Distribution Centre,
Newmarket Road, Bury St. Edmunds,
Suffolk IP33 3YB.
Telephone: +44 (0)1284 705705.
Fax: +44 (0)1284 703401.

www.musicsales.com

Printed in the EU.

Introduction

"Britain's greatest living composer..." was the accolade bestowed in 1929 by the Performing Right Society on Albert W. Ketèlbey (1875-1959). This was based on popularity as registered by the number of performances of his works. In particular, he had written a highly successful series of eighteen short pieces of descriptive music to accompany silent films, with such titles as *Bacchanale de Montmartre (for cabaret, orgy and riotous continental scenes)*. His speciality was producing the desired atmosphere by means of melodic directness coupled with effective and novel use of orchestral colour, carefully marketed with an explicit synopsis to ensure that the customers who bought the sheet music knew exactly what each piece was describing.

This combination of skills was the result of a varied career in music. He studied composition with local composers in his native Birmingham, before winning a scholarship to study at Trinity College in London. There, he was one of the outstanding pupils of his generation, and his academic credentials were later boosted when the college invited him to become an examiner. Among the jobs he subsequently took was musical director for light operas, musicals and revues, which demanded a focused approach to instant scene-setting. His skill at orchestration was polished through work for several publishers as an arranger of theatrical and orchestral music for the growing number of light orchestral combinations. Finally, he spent some twenty years working for Columbia records, as conductor, accompanist and musical factotum. In this job he met and worked with a wide variety of musicians, from opera singers to musical-hall artists, from concert pianists to military drummers, from members of symphony orchestras to jazz bands.

As a composer, his initial successes as a student led to little renown in the wider world, and he was approaching his fortieth year before he finally started to produce a series of popular classics with *The Phantom Melody*, which won a prize sponsored by the magazine Titbits, and the song *My Heart Still Clings To You*, winner of an Evening Standard competition. By this time a few of his works were being recorded by Columbia, and he was able to use his position to record many of his works soon after completion.

Between the Wars, the compositions of Ketèlbey were in the forefront of light music, not only in Britain, but across Europe and the Empire. The publishing firm Bosworth marketed his work vigorously, issuing many of his pieces with eye-catching pictorial covers which mirrored the catchy melodies contained inside. By the age of 51 he was earning enough from royalties to be able to retire from Columbia and devote his time to producing a handful of lucrative hits each year, doing an annual concert tour around the resorts, and spending the rest of the time out of the public eye in the south of France.

"Inexpensive pseudo-orientalism..." was one of the derogatory labels applied to Ketèlbey's music by critics envious of his success. Indeed, his view of the "East" was third-hand, seen through the eyes of Sullivan, Puccini and other composers working within the Western musical tradition. He exploited a package of musical effects, including unusual scales (pentatonic and flattened second) and unusual harmony (parallel fourths or fifths, even parallel augmented fifths at the start of *In a Chinese Temple Garden*). Colour effects, such as getting instrumentalists to sing or shout, were more innovative, probably influenced by the composer's work with dance bands. For all their exotic trappings, the oriental pieces each have sections depicting love scenes which are written in a traditional Western style not far removed from that of Elgar, with expressive melodic leaps and subtle harmonic support.

The composer's most commercially successful piece was ***In a Persian Market*** (1920). The publisher's preliminary advert announced it as an "educational novelty", with the unusual piano writing and explicit narrative aimed at brightening up keyboard lessons. These beggars are the musical descendants of those in Sullivan's opera *The Rose of Persia*, and Ketèlbey's Princess is clearly related to the princesses in *Stravinsky's Firebird*, both themes offspring of Russian parentage: a folksong used by Rimsky-Korsakov.

The oriental setting reappears in ***In a Chinese Temple Garden*** (1923), which the composer recorded for Columbia with several ensembles: the Court Symphony Orchestra, his own Concert Orchestra and the Silver Stars Band. The melody given to the "Incantation of the Priests" was taken from an early piano piece, *Morceau Pathétique.*

In the Mystic Land of Egypt (1931) was never recorded by the composer. Its melodic freshness and brilliant orchestration, however, have attracted several recent recordings.

The exotic background of ***With the Roumanian Gypsies*** (written by 1932, but only published in 1935), is closer to home, the style recalling the *Hungarian Rhapsodies* of Liszt. The cadenzas were written with a violin in mind, but the composer later reworked the piece for piano and orchestra, under the new name *Romany Rhapsody*.

By the mid 1920s, the market was so saturated with works bearing Ketèlbey's name, that he offered a group of six pieces to his publisher Bosworth under the pseudonym of André de Basque. Only two of these, including ***A Japanese Carnival*** (1927), were accepted, while a third was later reworked as a concert piece for piano with orchestra under the title *Sunbeams and Butterflies*, with Ketèlbey's own name on the title page.

Another example of reworking comes in ***By the Blue Hawaiian Waters*** (1927). The section marked "The Dance of the Betrothal Ceremony" was taken note-for-note from a dance called Wonga in the play *Ye Gods*, produced in 1916. The Hawaiian atmosphere is evoked in the third bar and elsewhere by the imitation of the Hawaiian guitar, a steel-stringed instrument with a sliding fret mechanism which characteristically produces expressive swoops between notes.

There are conflicting accounts of the origins of ***In a Monastery Garden***. The composer himself spoke in later years of being inspired by a motor-ride past a monastery in North Yorkshire around 1912, and the piece is dedicated to Enrico Scoma, who conducted an orchestra in Bridlington. In fact, the manuscript of the piano version was given to a Franciscan friar, Brother Edgar Larway, who claimed that Ketèlbey had visited him at Chilworth Priory in Surrey around 1910. A recording was issued as early as May 1914, but the printed music had to wait until the following year, the synopsis being added several years later. I have consulted Brother Edgar's manuscript in preparing this edition.

Fairies of the Stream (1919) was advertised by Bosworth as "a really brilliant sparkling waltz of the Durand type... It is exceedingly pretty".

Jungle Drums (1926) shows the influence of the years of tuition in classical composition, with interesting use of melodic development and tonality. The first section consists of short phrase-units presented in different keys, while the main theme is gradually evolved, occurring first as a brief countermelody, only reaching its full form at its third appearance, and eventually being condensed to a shortened version in the final section.

Sanctuary of the Heart (1924) is a masterpiece of religious expression, with the accompanying poem "I wandered alone in a strange land" written by the composer. He had been brought up in the Church of England, and as choirboy and later organist, would have been familiar with the Psalms in the Book of Common Prayer. He borrows the phrase "In a strange land" from Psalm 137 *By the waters of Babylon*, while Psalm 114 *When Israel came out of Egypt* not only has the words "strange" and "sanctuary" in close proximity, but is traditionally sung in the Church of England to a chant called *Tonus Peregrinus*, meaning "wanderer tune". The Jewish background is reinforced by quoting the *Kol Nidrei*, a chant used in the Jewish liturgy on the Eve of the Day of Atonement. Thus this spiritually uplifting piece unites the references to escape, exile and diaspora with Jewish and Christian search for redemption.

The Clock and the Dresden Figures was written as a novelty item for one of the composer's concert tours, first performed in February 1930 with the Ketèlbey himself playing the piano, to the accompaniment of the Band of the Royal Horse Guards.

The remaining five pieces in this collection belong to the genre of intermezzo. ***In the Moonlight*** (1919) and ***Wedgwood Blue*** (1920) are straightforward pieces with clear-cut structure and repetitive rhythms. ***Gallantry*** (1921) and ***Love and the Dancer*** (1943) are each graced with a short synopsis, but share similar traits. Several sections of *Gallantry* were slightly simplified after its initial publication, and this edition follows the revisions. ***Italian Twilight*** was written when the composer was in his mid-seventies and first performed in 1950. It has a more relaxed form, starting and ending in different keys.

This edition has been newly prepared from the original editions published by Bosworth, apart from *In a Monastery Garden*, which was published by Joseph Larway.

In A Persian Market

Intermezzo-Scene

Composer's synopsis

The camel-drivers gradually approach the market; the cries of beggars for "Back-sheesh" are heard amid the bustle. The beautiful princess enters carried by her servants, (she is represented by a languorous theme, given at first to clarinet and cello, then repeated by full orchestra) – she stays to watch the jugglers and snake-charmer. The Caliph now passes through the market and interrupts the entertainment, the beggars are heard again, the princess prepares to depart and the caravan resumes its journey; the themes of the princess and the camel-drivers are heard faintly in the distance and the market-place becomes deserted.

*Back-sheesh = money.

*Empshi = get away.

Ped. Ped. Ped.

Ped. Ped. Ped. Ped.

Ped. Ped. Ped.

Ped. Ped.

Ped.

sonore e largamente
ff sostenuto
Ped.

8va
Ped.
The jugglers in the market-place
(8)
ff
f

ff
Ped.

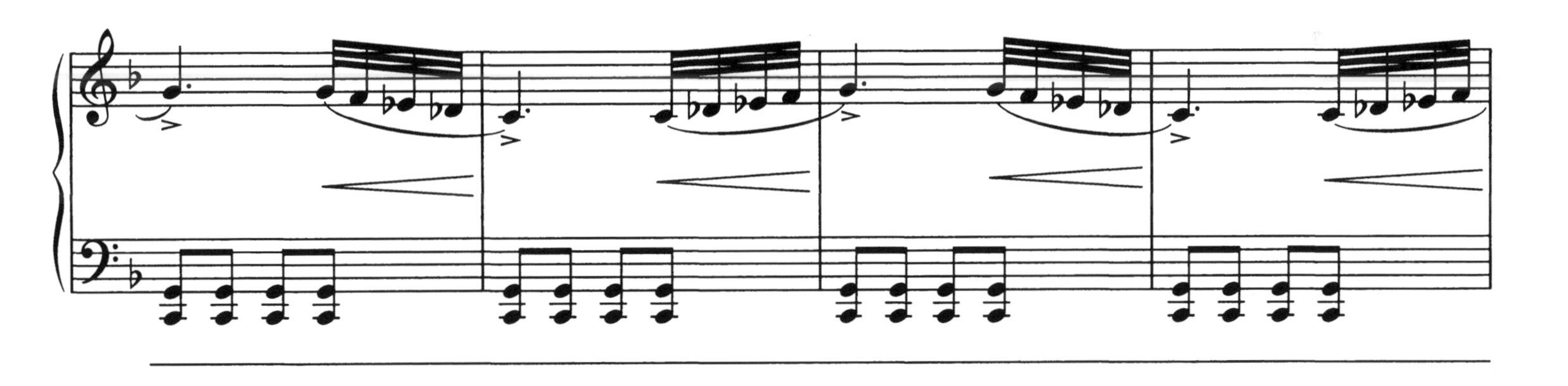

(Trumpets)
ff

The Caliph passes through the market-place
ff marziale
meno f
dim.
8va
The beggars are heard again
(Sing) Back-sheesh, back - sheesh, Al - - lah, Back-sheesh, back - sheesh,
f
Al - - lah, Back-sheesh, back - sheesh, Al - - lah,
Emp - shi emp - shi emp - shi!
The Princess prepares to depart
mf sonore

poco a poco dim.
una corda
poco rit.
p
pp

8va
f marcato
f
(8)
mf
8va
dim.

pp espress.
Ped.
più p
The market-place becomes deserted
pp
sf

Dedicated to my friend Signor Enrico Scoma

In A Monastery Garden

Characteristic Intermezzo

Composer's synopsis

The first theme represents a poet's reverie in the quietude of the monastery garden amidst beatific surroundings – the calm serene atmosphere, the leafy trees, and the singing birds. The second theme in the minor, expresses the more "personal" note of sadness, of appeal and contrition. Presently the monks are heard chanting the "Kyrie Eleison" (which should be sung by the orchestra) with the organ playing and the chapel-bell ringing. The first theme is now heard in a quieter manner as if it had become more ethereal and distant; the singing of the monks is again heard – it becomes louder and more insistent, bringing the piece to a conclusion in a glow of exultation.

poco rit.
p
pp
tr
L.H.
Sopra
L.H.
Sopra
Più mosso
mf
con Ped.
accel. e cresc.
rall.
ten.
rit.
f
pp
a tempo
mf
accel. e cresc.
rall.
ten.
rit.
p
pp

Tempo I
p marcato melodia
con Ped.
poco rit.
a tempo

poco rit.
Ped.
Chant of the Monks
Religioso e sostenuto
Ky - ri - e E - le - i - son, Ky - ri -
p (a là Organ)
Bell
8va
con Ped.
f
-e E - le - i - son, E - lei - son.
dim.
8va
Bell

Ky - - ri - - - e, E - - - le - - - i - - - - son, Ky - ri -
mf
Bell
8va
L.H.
f
- e, E - - - le - - i - son, E - lei - - son.
dim.
pp
Tempo I
con Ped.

poco rit.
a tempo
molto legato
pp
mf
poco rit.
a tempo
pp
con 8va
Ky - - ri - - - e, E - le - i - - son.
mf sostenuto
Bell
8va
con Ped.
Ped.
Bell
Ped.
allargando
Ky - - rie, Ky - - rie, E - lei - - son.
f
ff
f
ff
lunga pausa
sf
pp
Bell
8va
Ped.
simile

In A Chinese Temple-Garden

Oriental Phantasy

Composer's synopsis

After a few bars' characteristic introduction, the incantation of the priests in the temple – the perfume of incense floats on the air – a melody (given to cello, viola and oboe with pizzicato accompaniment) represents two lovers – a Manchu wedding-procession passes noisily by – a street disturbance ensues amongst the coolies (founded on an actual Chinese scale) – the beating of the gong in the temple restores quietude – the incantation of the priests is heard again – the lovers' song (amidst the singing of birds) brings the piece to a conclusion with a brief quotation from the temple and coolies' music.

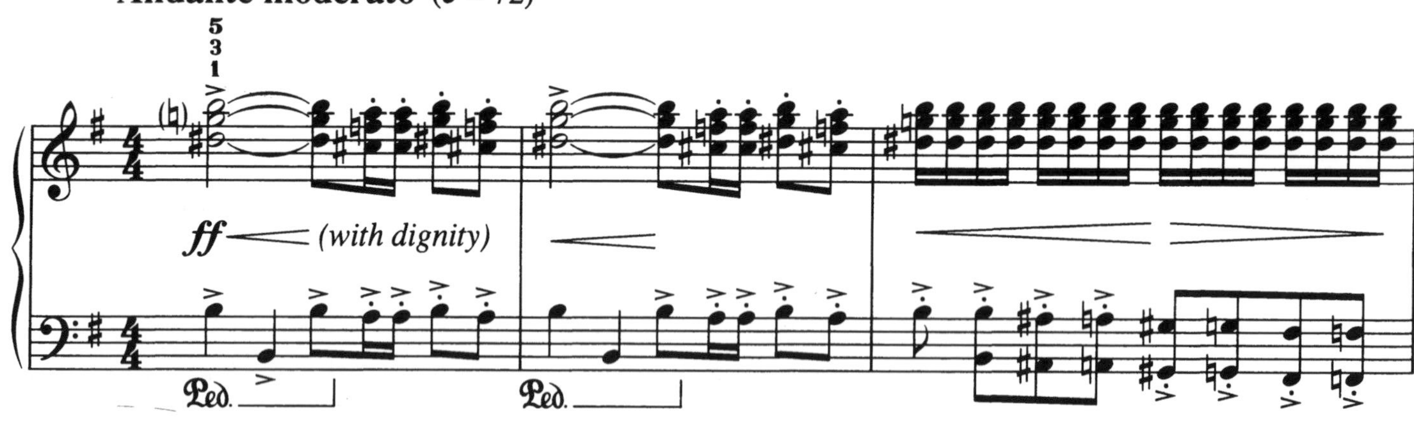

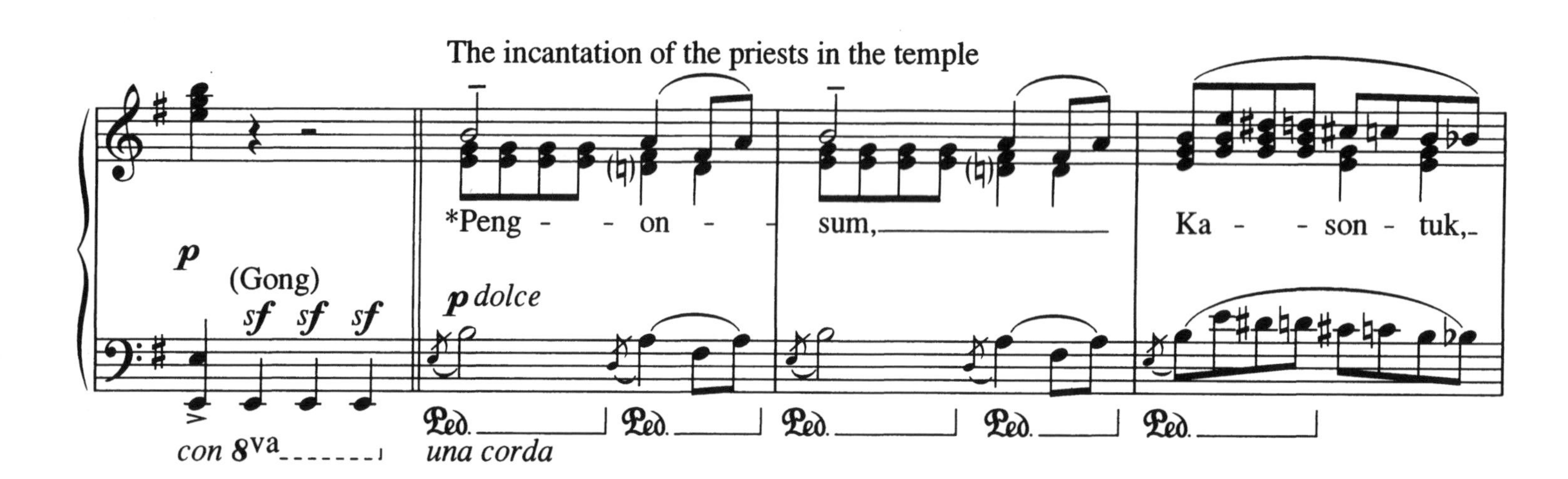

*"Chinese (Canton dialect) means: Peace of mind increase faith and imploringly worship". (A.W.K.)

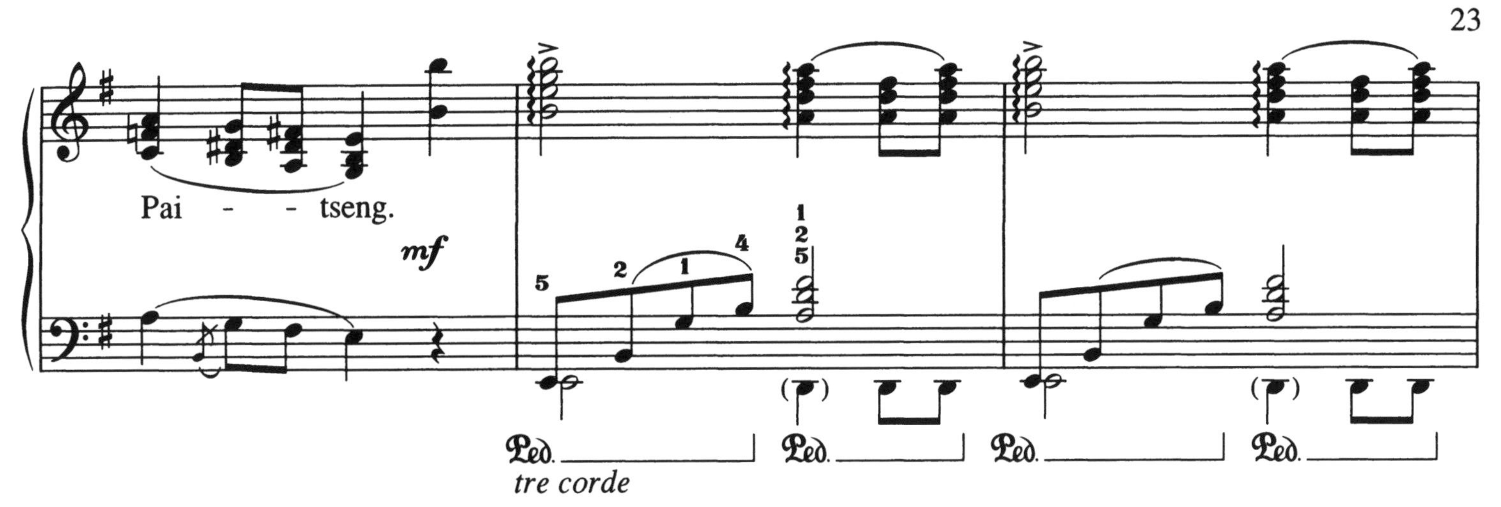
Pai - - tseng.
mf
5 2 1 4
1 2 5
tre corde

The perfume of incense floats on the air
5 3 1
con 8va

pp
pp
Ped.
Ped.
Ped.
Ped.
con 8va

The song of the lovers
mf marcato
tre corde
con molto espress.
Ped.
Ped.

Ped.
Ped.
Ped.

rit.
a tempo con molto espress.
sostenuto
Ped.
Ped.
Ped.
Ped.
Ped.
Ped.

Ped. simile
rit.
ten.
a tempo
A Manchu wedding-procession passes by
più mosso
ff
Ped.
cresc.
Ped.
8

ff
Ped.
Ped.
dim.
p
A street disturbance ensues amongst the coolies
mf
Ped.
Ped.
Ped.
accel. poco a poco
8va
ff
Ped.
Ped.
Ped.

accel. poco a poco
accel. molto
(8)
ff
Ped.

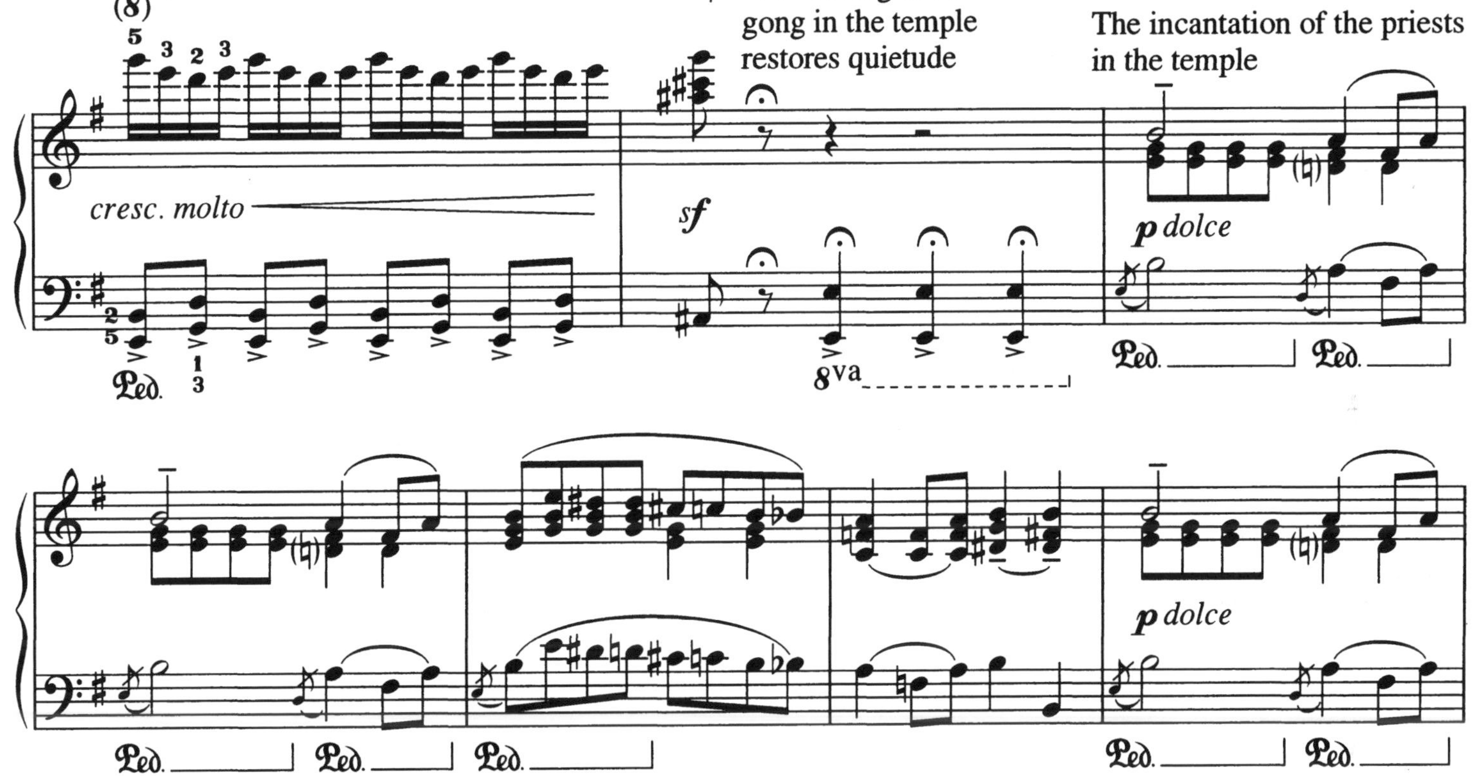
(8)
The beating of the gong in the temple restores quietude
The incantation of the priests in the temple
cresc. molto
sf
p dolce
8va
Ped.

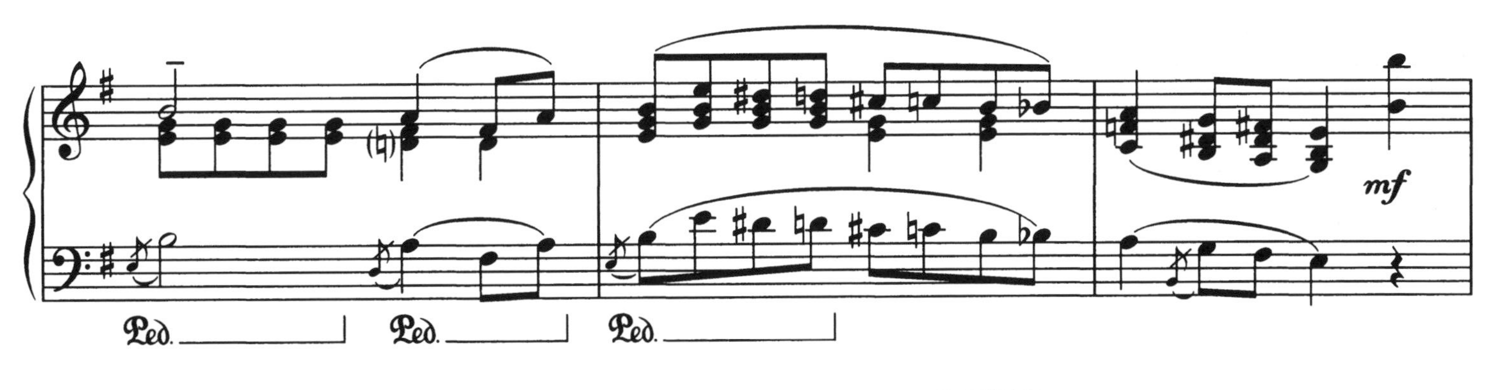
mf
Ped.

Ped.

molto rit.
pp
Ped.
Ped.
Ped.
Ped.
Ped.
The lovers' song
dolcissimo e sostenuto
Ped.
una corda
Ped.
Ped. simile
rit.
a tempo
f
con Ped.
tre corde

rit. molto
a tempo
ten.
ten.
f
pp dolce
a tempo con moto
ff
Più mosso
f
accel. al fine
cresc.
cresc. molto
accel. molto
8va

Sanctuary Of The Heart

Méditation Religieuse

Composer's synopsis

The picture in the composer's mind when writing this piece was that of a lonely wanderer in a foreign land, hearing again an old religious melody (the "Kol Nidrei") that was familiar in childhood, and the memories evoked by the old associations bring great solace and comfort to the heart of the poor exile.

Andante sostenuto

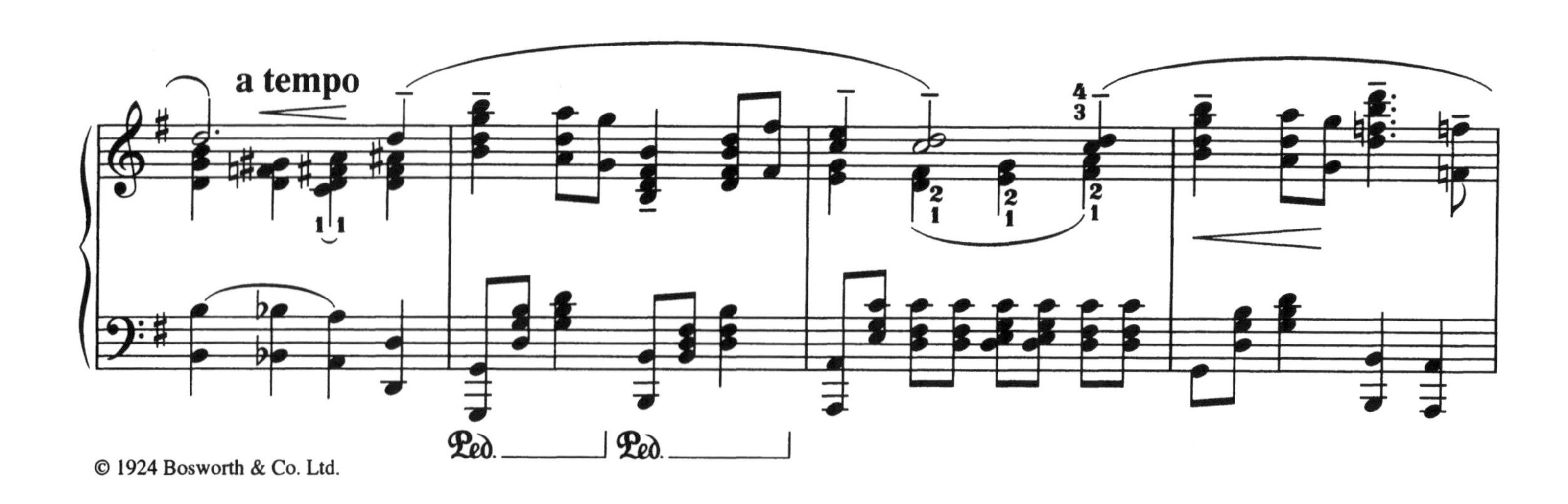

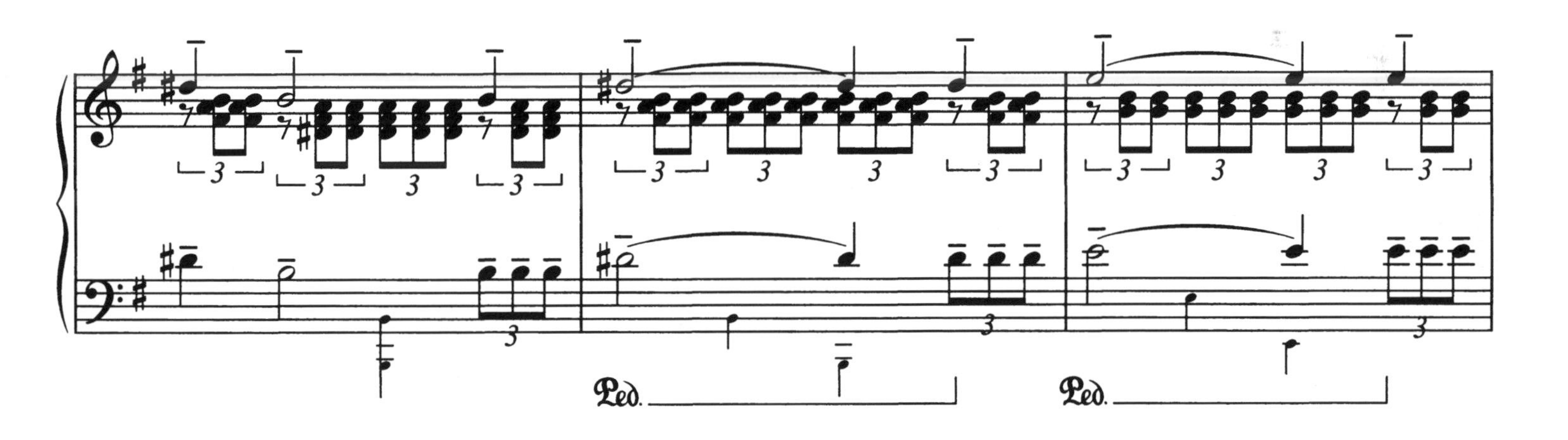

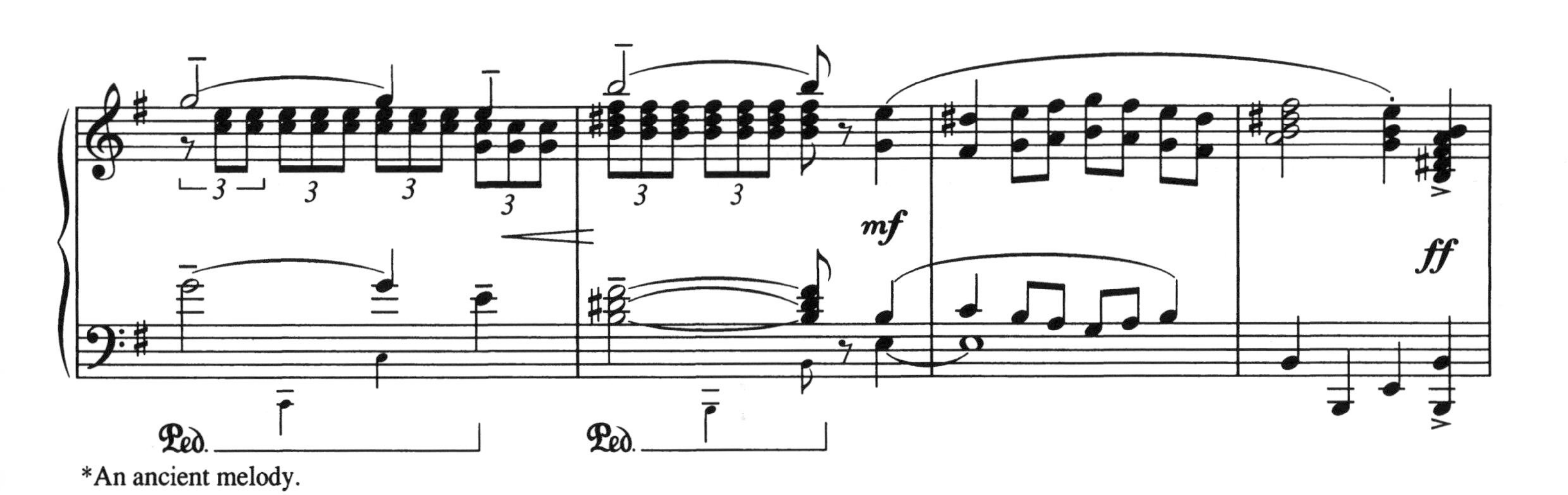

*An ancient melody.

Grandioso
8
Ped.
Ped.
con Ped.
Ped.
Ped.
con Ped.
8va
(8)
Ped.

rit.
3
3
mf
Ped.

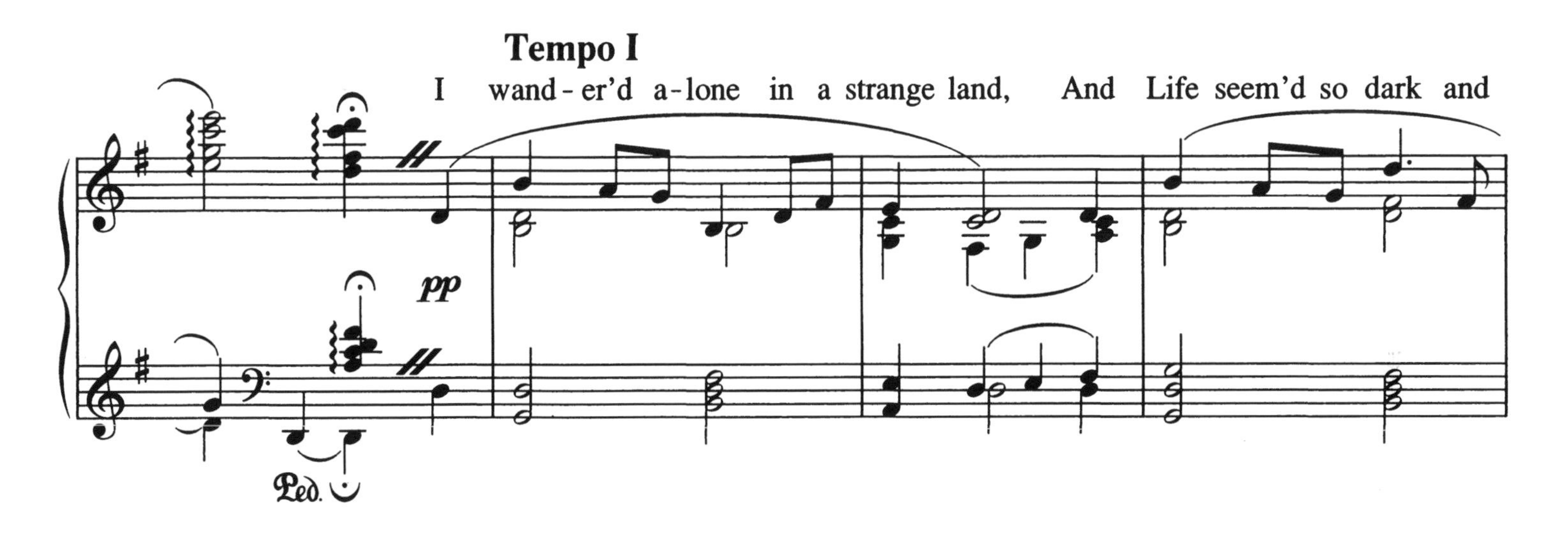
Tempo I
I wand - er'd a - lone in a strange land, And Life seem'd so dark and
pp
Ped.

rit.
dear, When the sound of a voice seem'd to call me And brought to my mind a mem - 'ry
ten.

a tempo
dear; It told of the Joy and the Glad - ness That comes from the One a -

rit.
- bove: "Oh Lord, hear our pray'r, Take a - way all our care, And fill all our hearts with
Love."
Grandioso
cresc. molto
L.H.
ff
simile
rit.
ten.

a tempo
p
allargando
ff
Ped.
con Ped.
rit.
a tempo
rit. molto
fff

In The Mystic Land Of Egypt

Composer's synopsis

A detachment of native soldiers approaches and passes through the village, then a song from a boat on the Nile is heard softly across the water; a short passage depicting an Arab playing his pipe leads to a repetition of the song-melody. The soldiers return and some of them sing the song in harmony. A few bars of the melody bring the piece to a quiet conclusion.

A detachment of native soldiers approach and pass through the village

Con moto (♩ = 108) *(quasi marcia)*

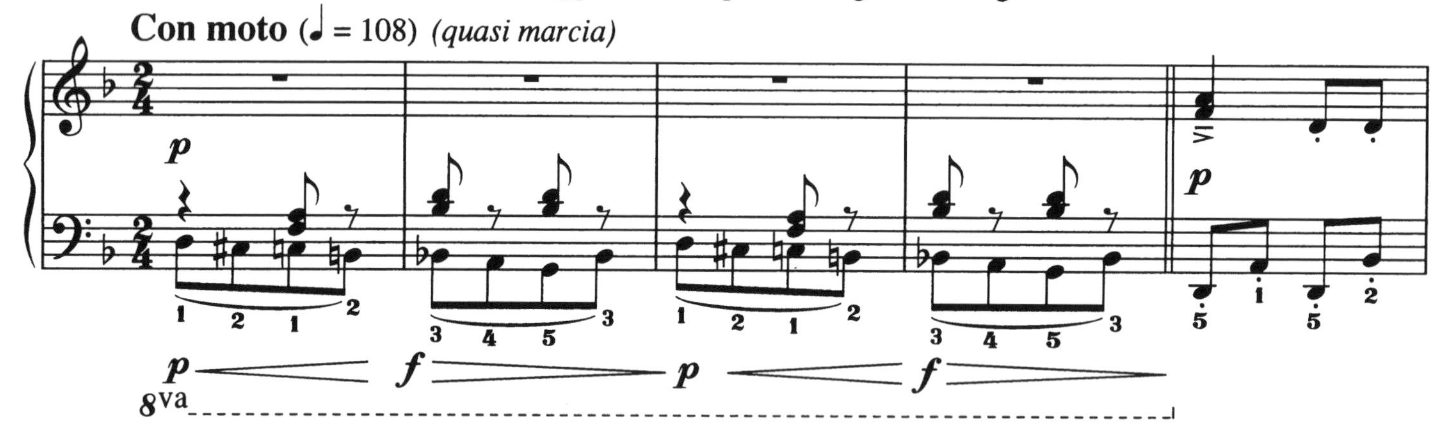

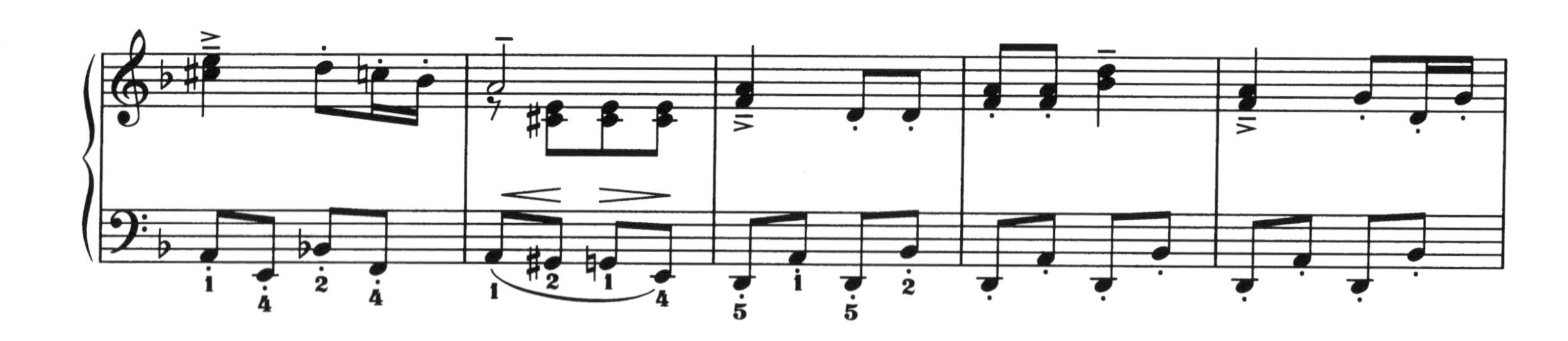

f
cresc.
sf
fff

8va
(8)
f
mf
p
pp
mf

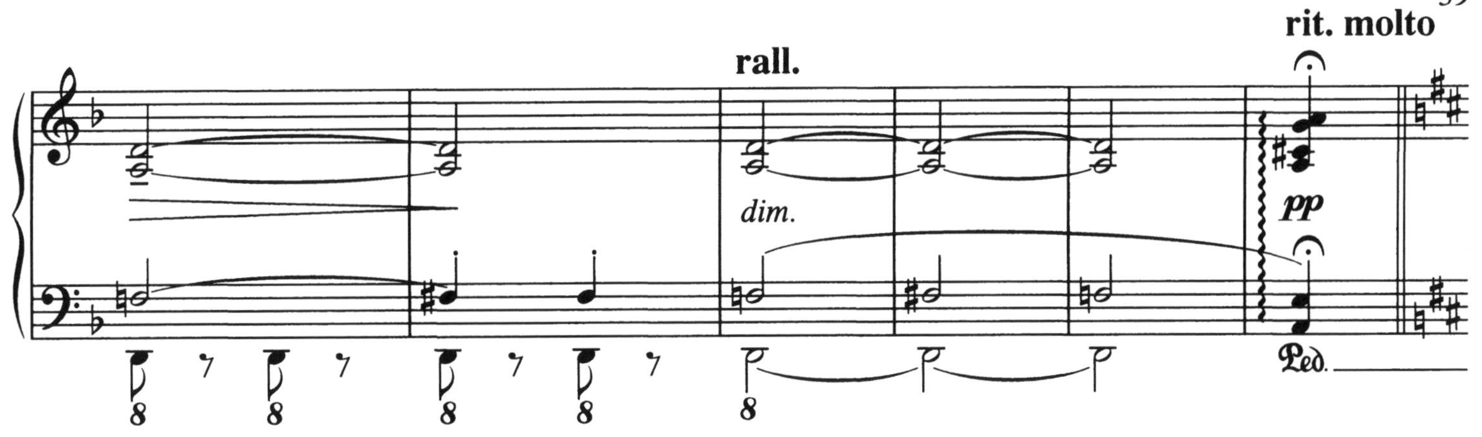

A song is heard from a boat on the Nile.

Andante espressivo

40

a tempo

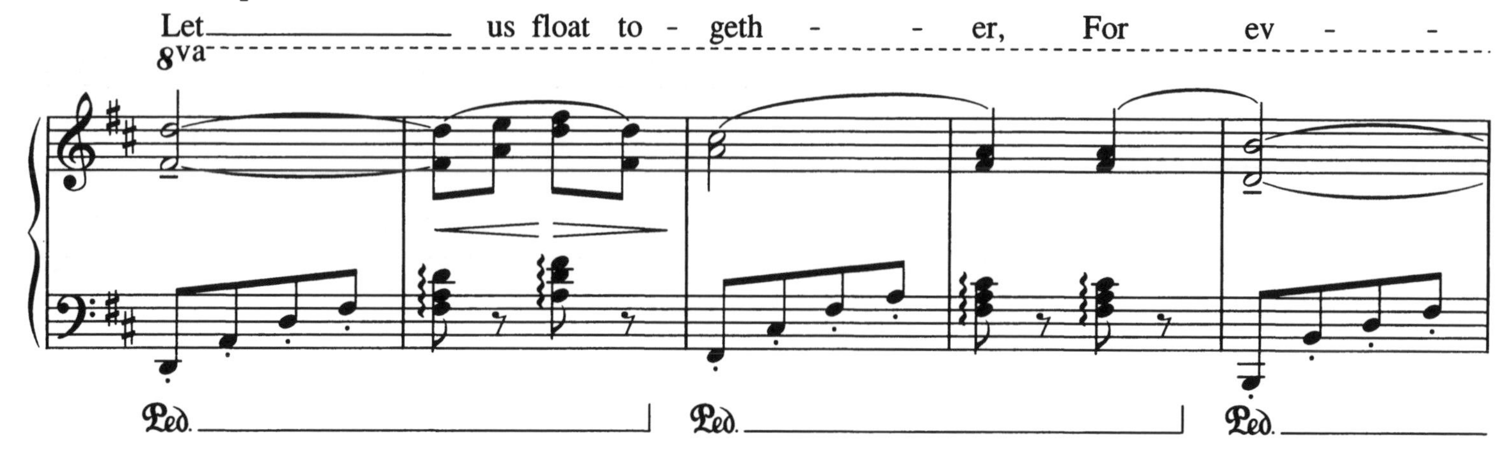
Let us float to - geth - - er, For ev - -
8va
Ped.
Ped.
Ped.

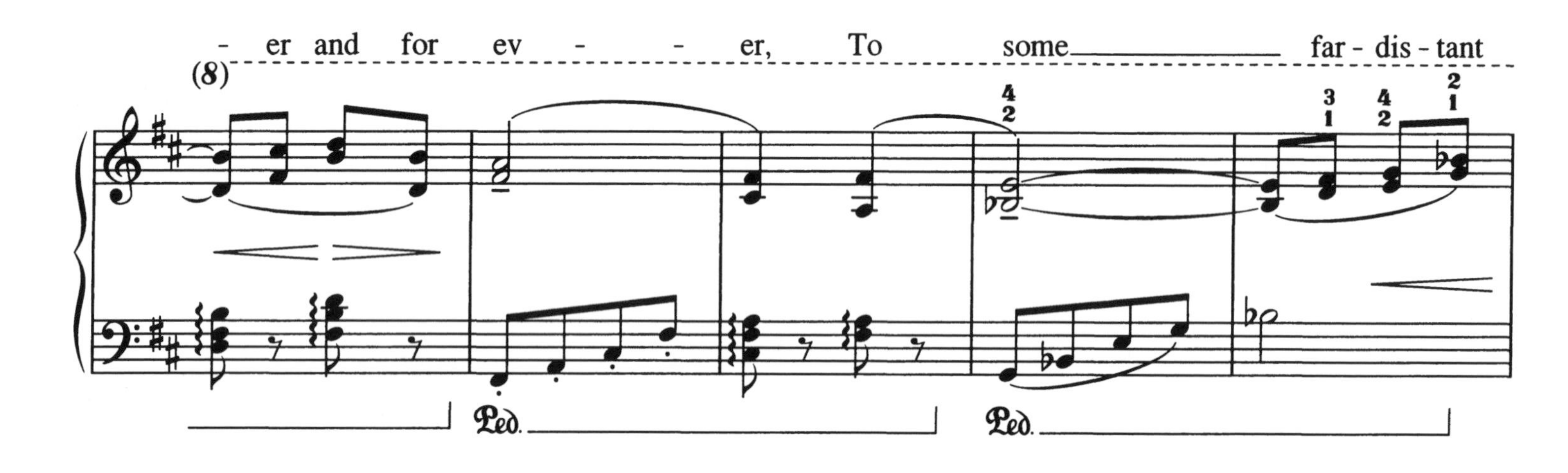
- er and for ev - - er, To some far - dis - tant
(8)
Ped.
Ped.

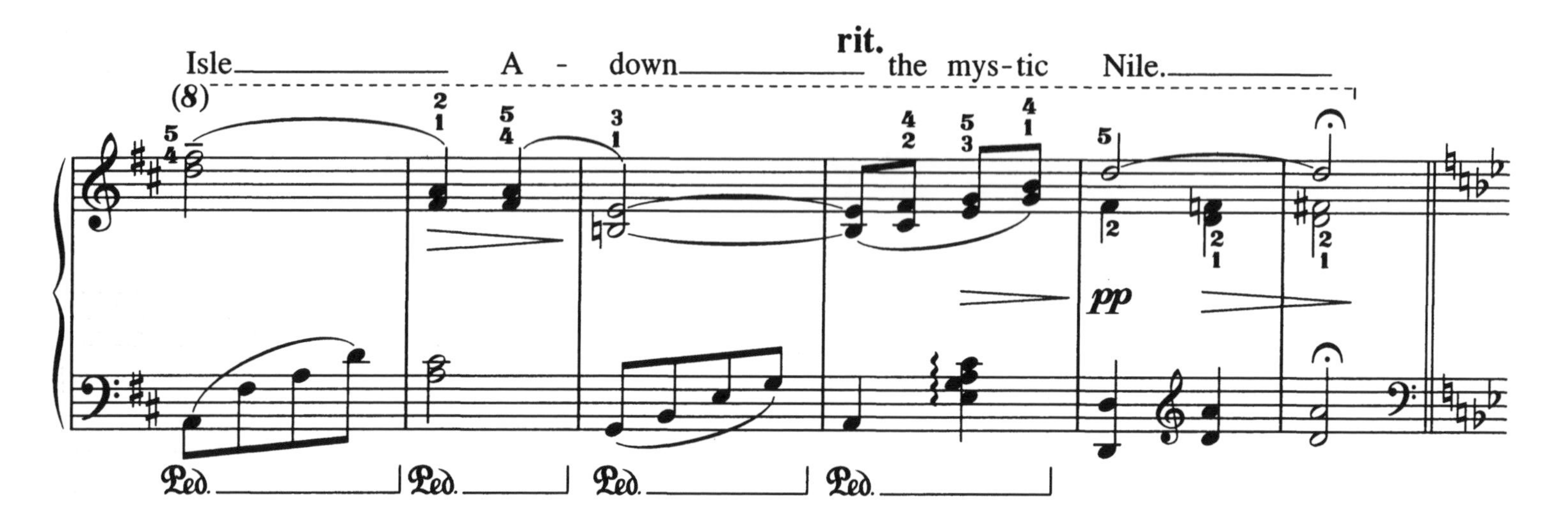
rit.
Isle A - down the mys - tic Nile.
(8)
pp
Ped.
Ped.
Ped.
Ped.

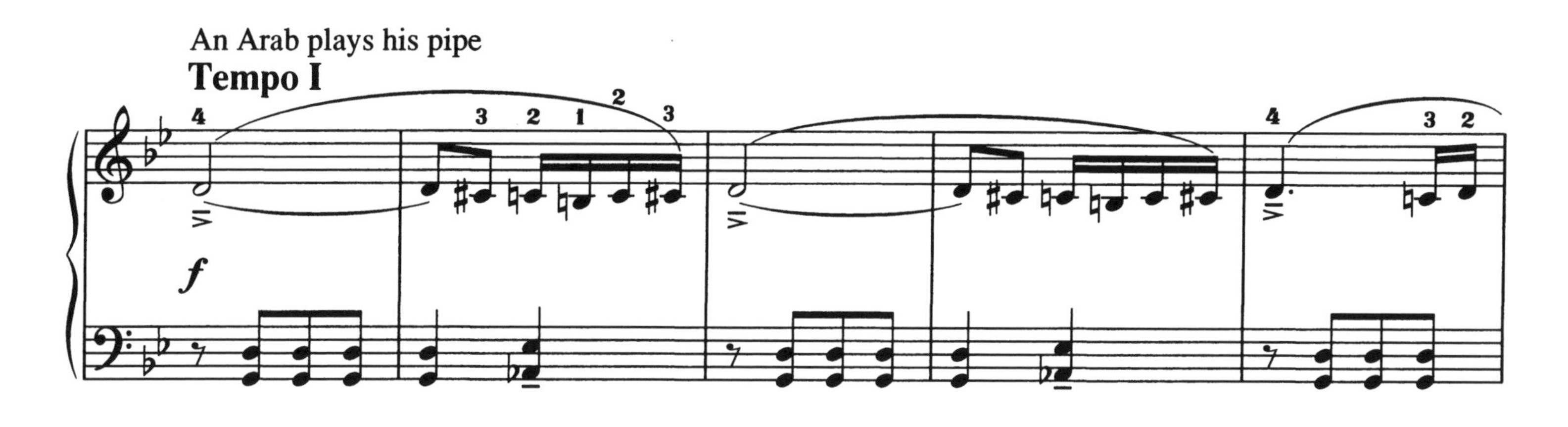
An Arab plays his pipe
Tempo I
f

mf
f
mf
f
f
mf
f
rit.
rit. molto
mf
mf
cresc.
f

Andante
ff sostenuto
rit.
a tempo
ff sostenuto
dim.

rit.
8va
p
pp
Ped.
Ped.
Ped.
Ped.
The soldiers return
Tempo I
p
f
8va
cresc.

ff
cresc.
ff
8va
(8)
rit.
f
Andante
mf
Ped.
Ped.
Ped.

rit.
a tempo
p
f
dim.
Ped.

rit.
a tempo
p
pp
f melodia espressivo
Ped.
rit.
a tempo
Ped.
rit.
8va
ff
pp
Ped.
8va

With The Roumanian Gypsies

Phantasie

Composer's synopsis

This work opens with a few of the Gypsy Orchestra playing a Romany Love-Song; this attracts attention and they burst into a characteristically Tzigane melody; a shepherd's pipe is now heard from the hills and leads into the Love-Song, variously treated through changing keys. A Gypsy Dance now follows, and with a quotation from the Love-Song, brings this work to an excited finish.

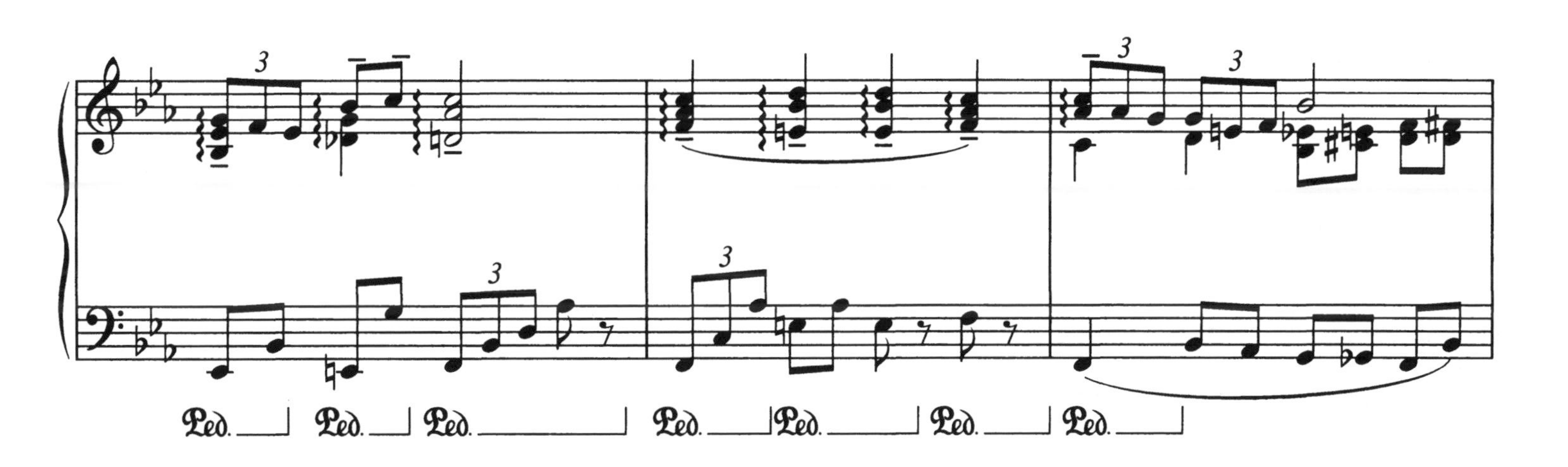

rit.
a tempo
f
Ped.

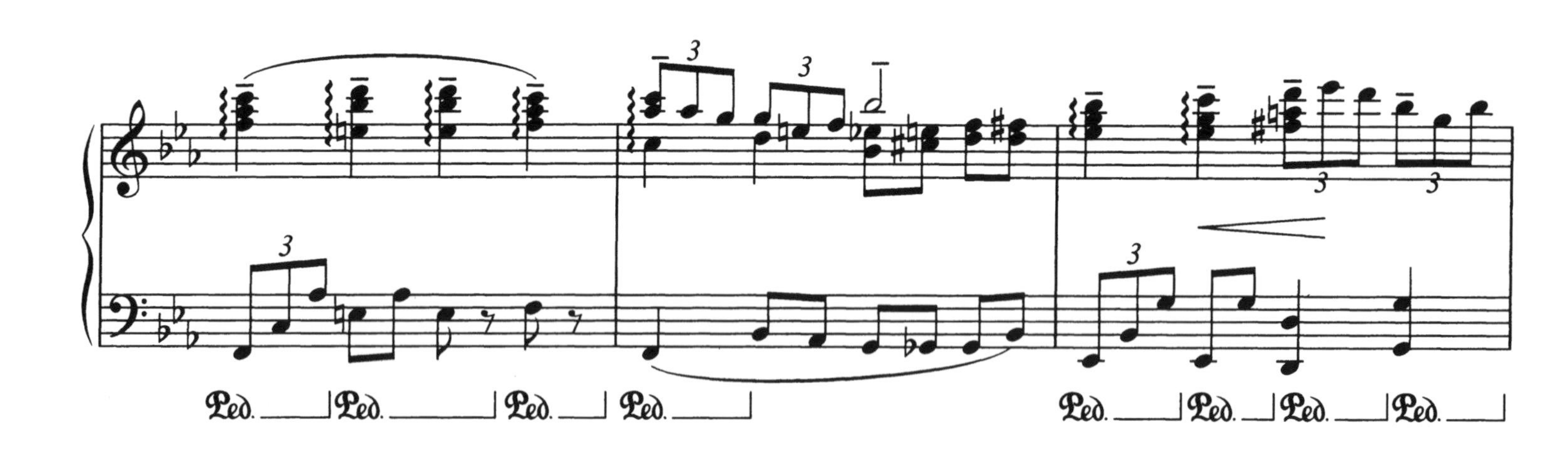
Ped.

accel.
Ped.

Cadenza brillante
Ped.

con fuoco
sf

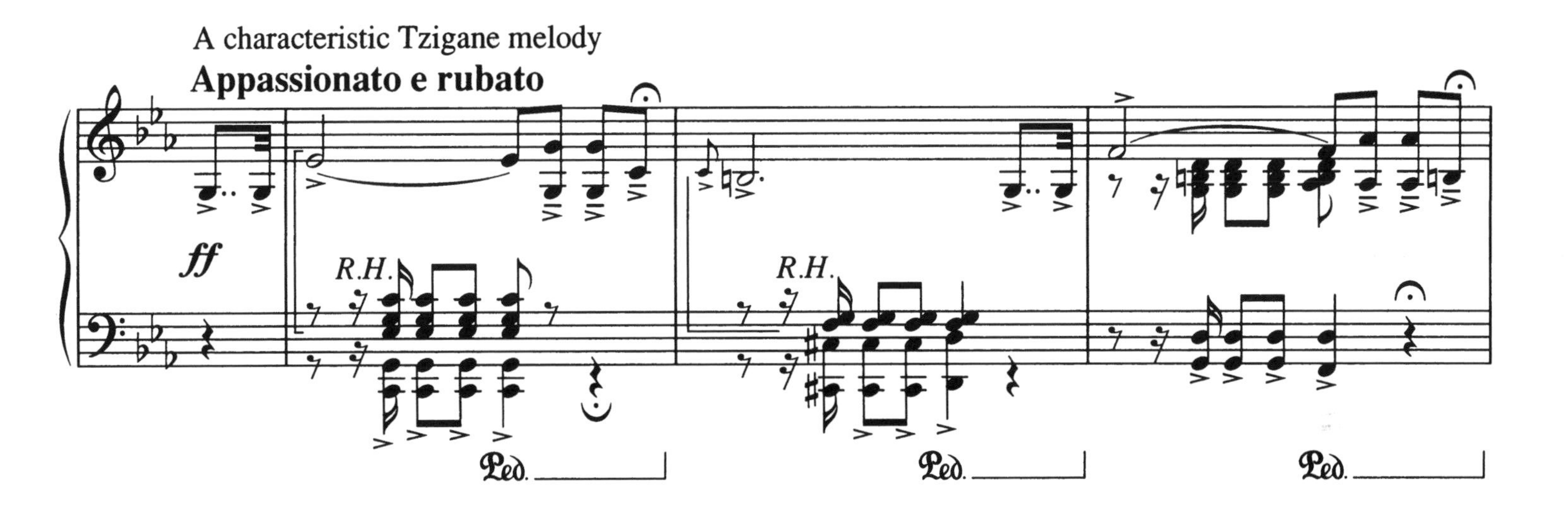
A characteristic Tzigane melody
Appassionato e rubato
ff
R.H.
R.H.

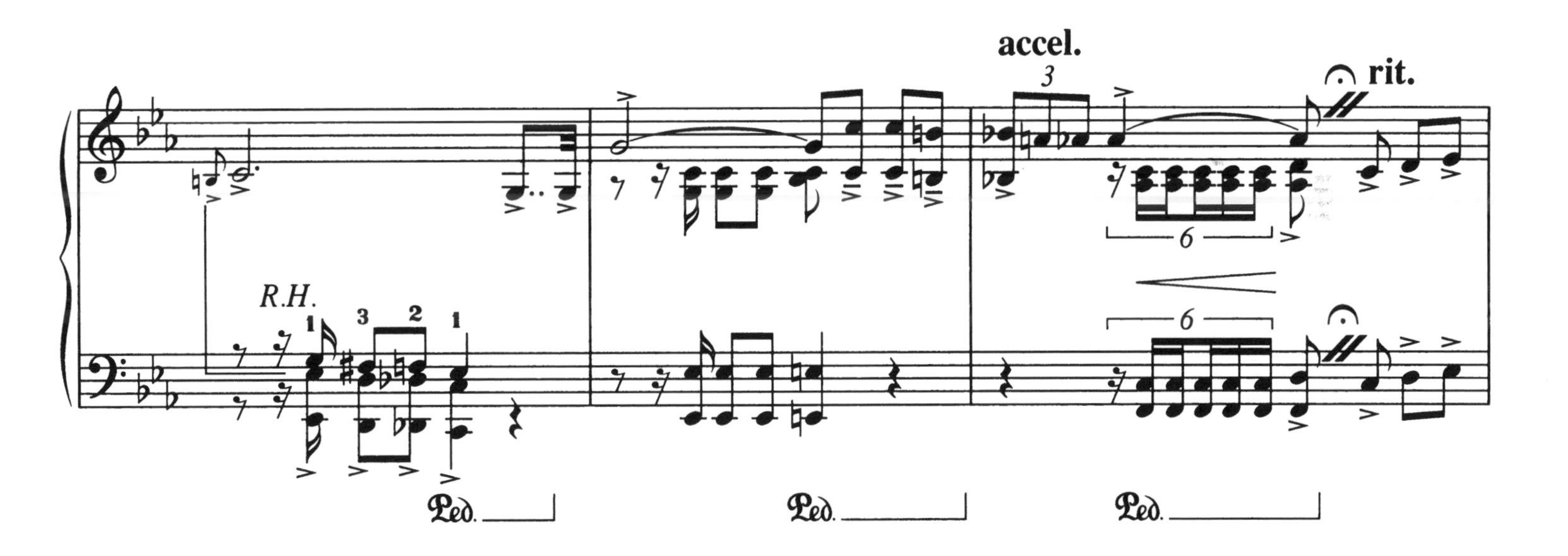
accel.
rit.
R.H.

a tempo
Cadenza brillante

Poco più mosso
ten.
p
grazioso
tr
ff
Ped.

rit.
a tempo
ff
Ped.
8va
rit.
ff

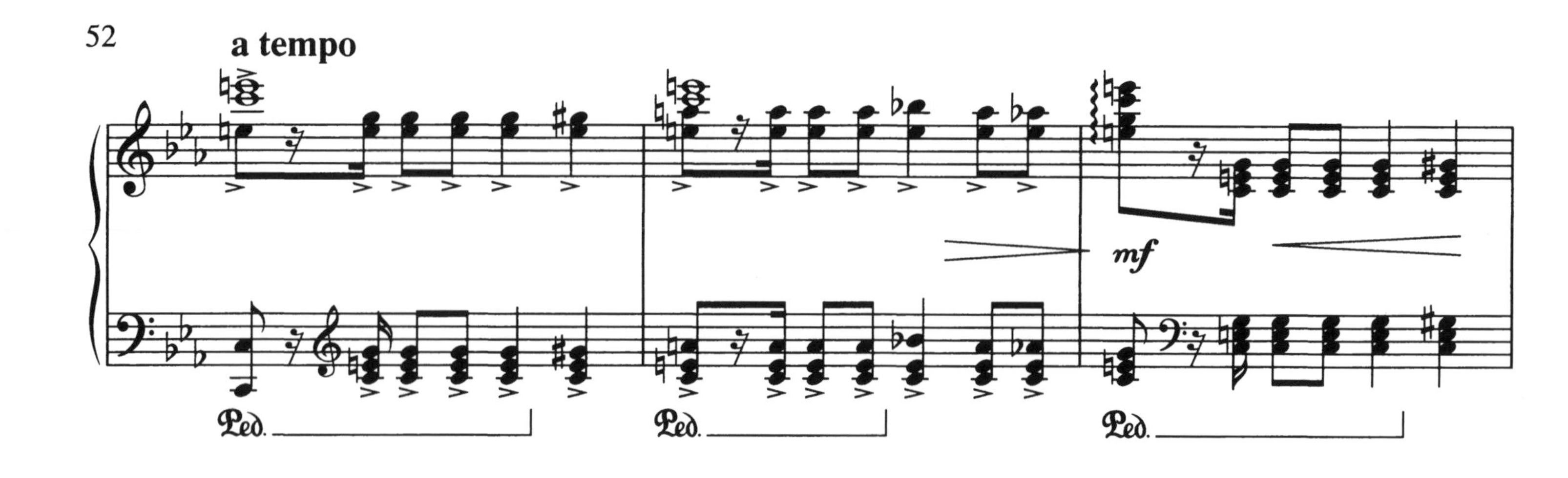
a tempo
mf
Ped.
Ped.
Ped.

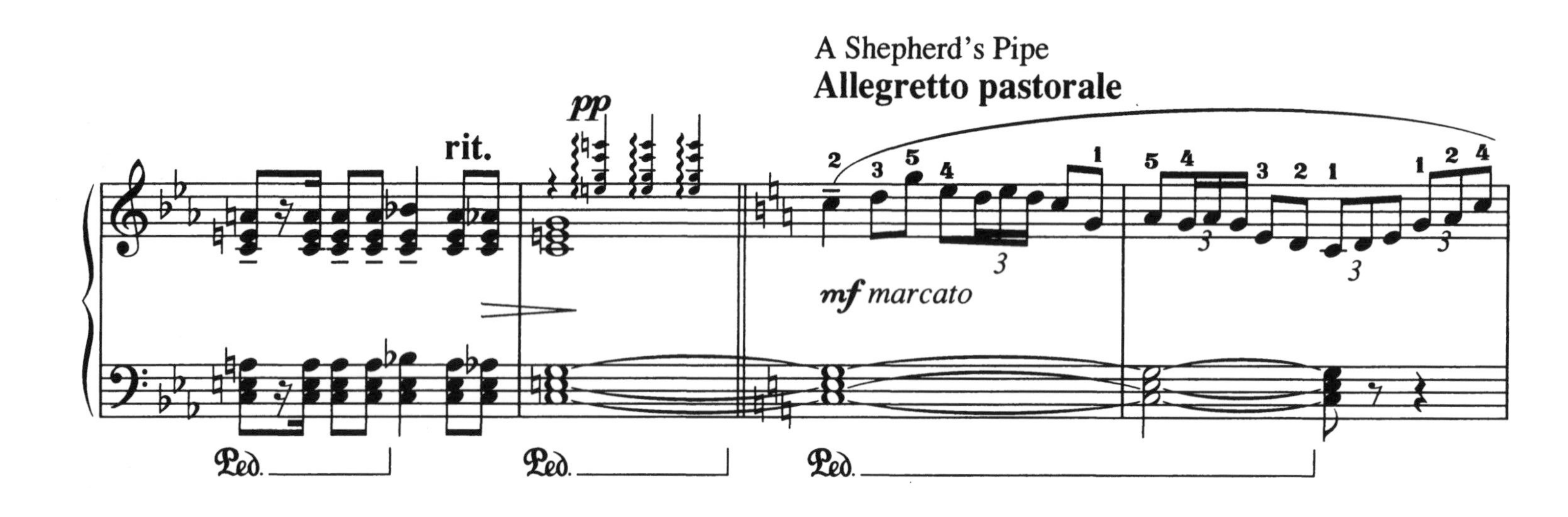
rit.
pp
A Shepherd's Pipe
Allegretto pastorale
mf marcato
Ped.
Ped.
Ped.

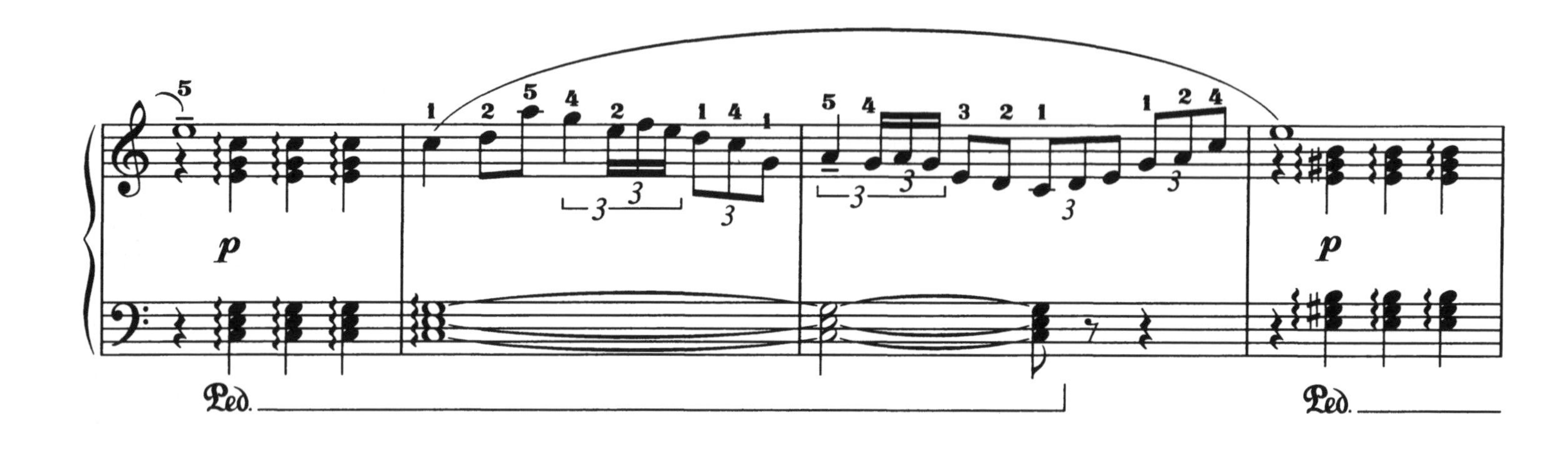
p
p
Ped.
Ped.

rit.
Ped.
Ped.
Ped.

The Romany Love-Song
Moderato espressivo
pp
pp
mf
Ped.
melodia espressivo marcato
rit.
a tempo
melodia
mf
f
Ped.
Ped.
ff
Sonore e legato
f
Ped.
Ped.
Ped.
Ped.
Ped.
Ped.
Ped.
Ped.

Ped.
Ped.
Ped.
Ped.
Ped.
Ped.
Ped.
Ped.

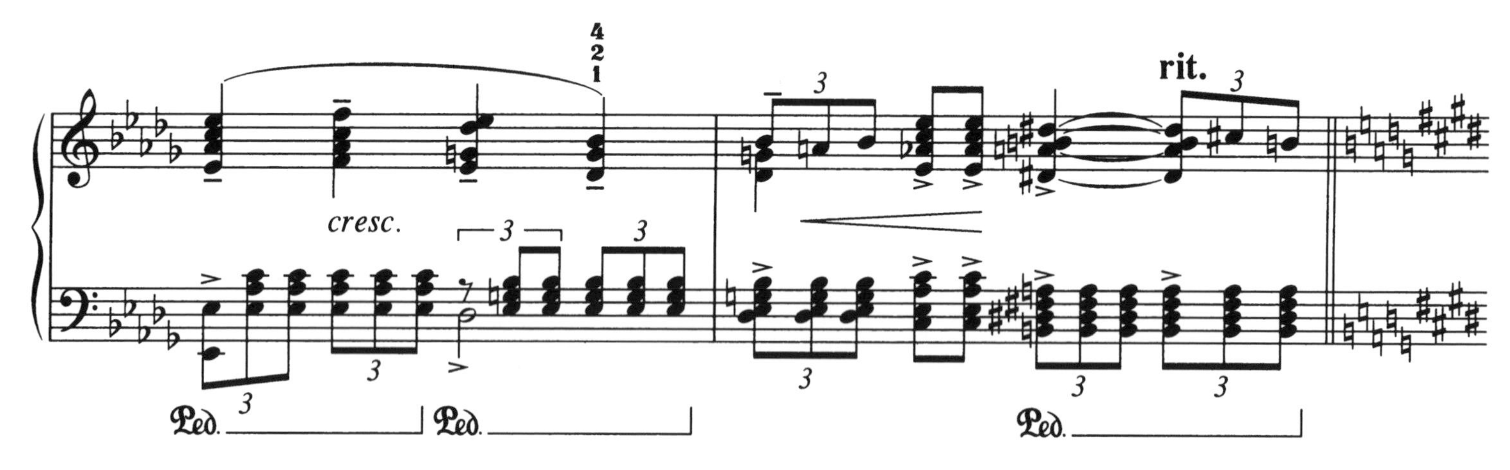
cresc.
rit.
Ped.
Ped.
Ped.

Più mosso
ff appassionato
Ped.
Ped.
Ped.
Ped.
Ped.
Ped.
Ped.

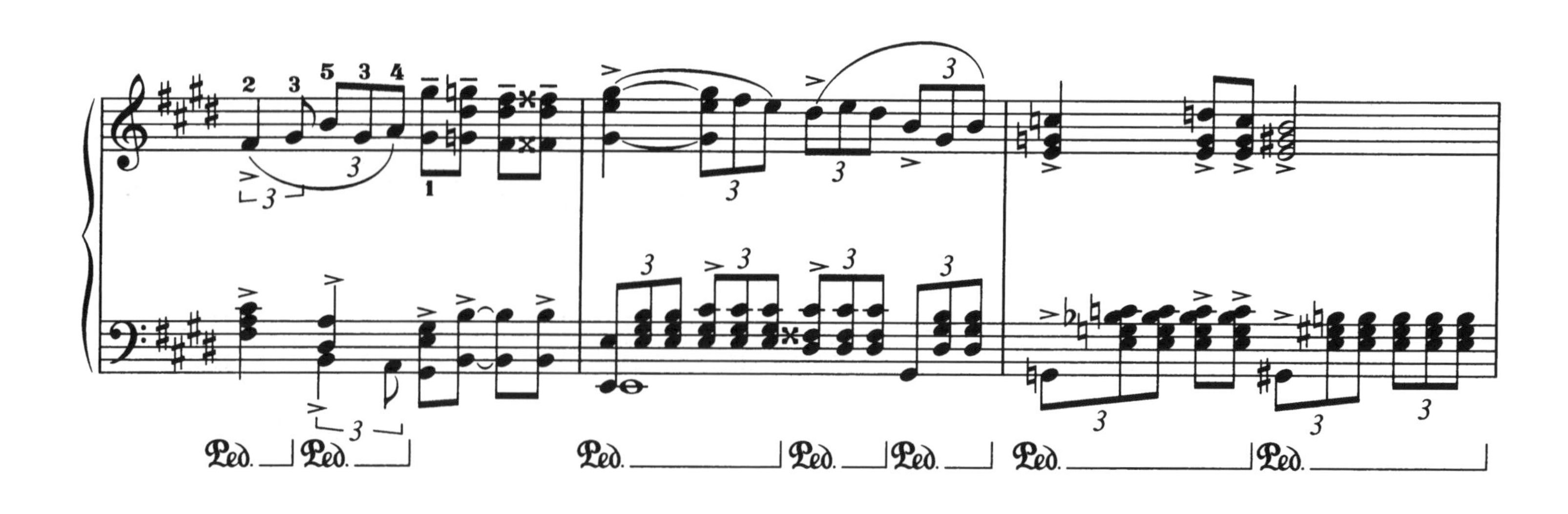
Ped.
Ped.
Ped.
Ped.
Ped.
Ped.
Ped.

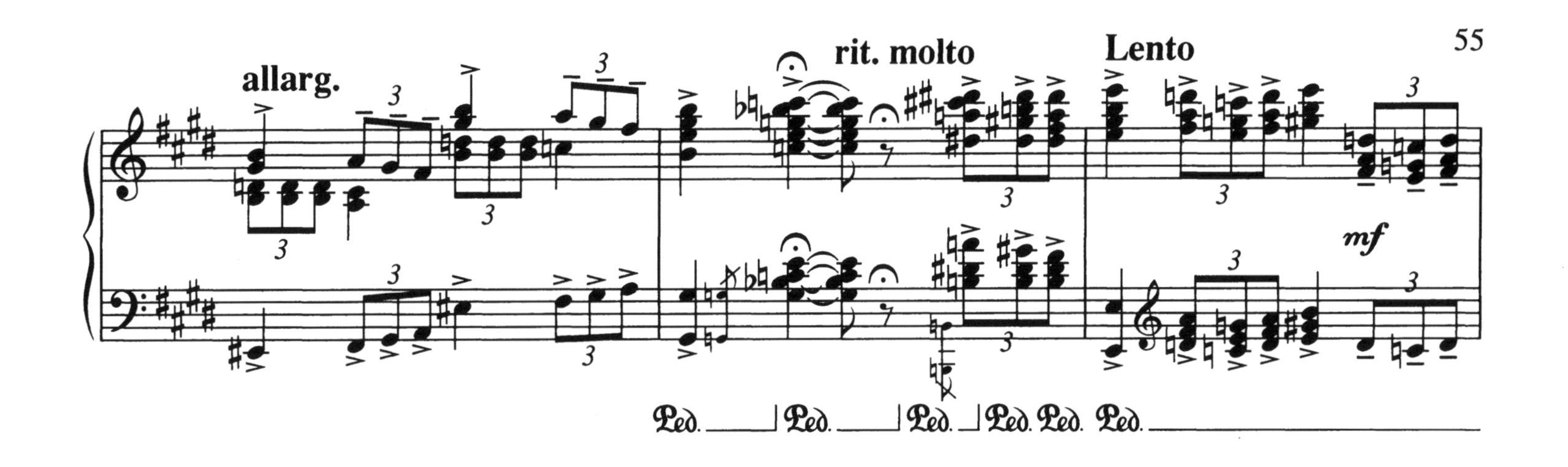
allarg.
rit. molto
Lento
mf

Vivace alla danza
pp
p

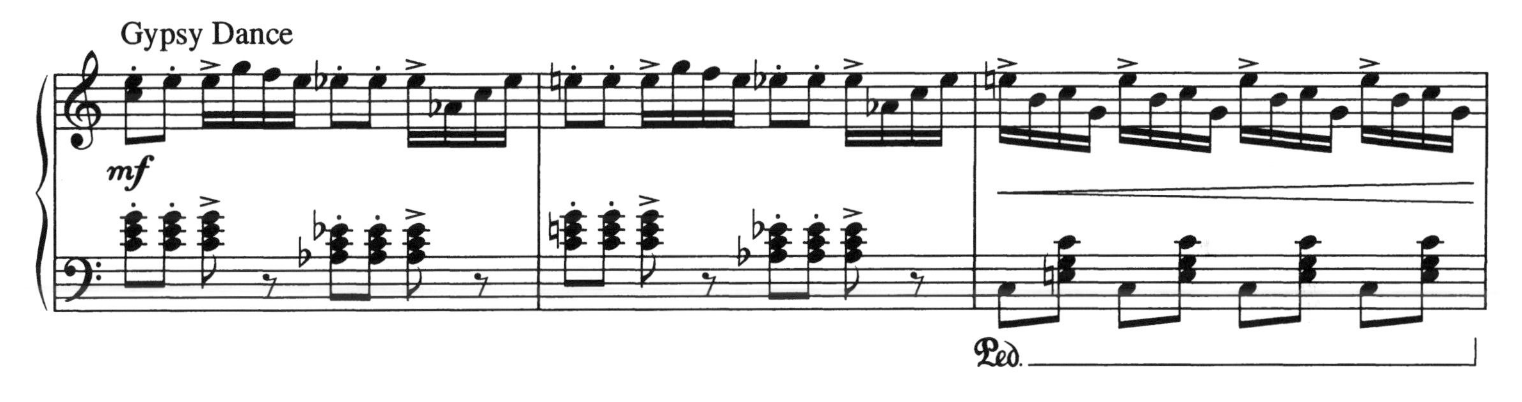
Gypsy Dance
mf

ff
Ped.
ff
1.

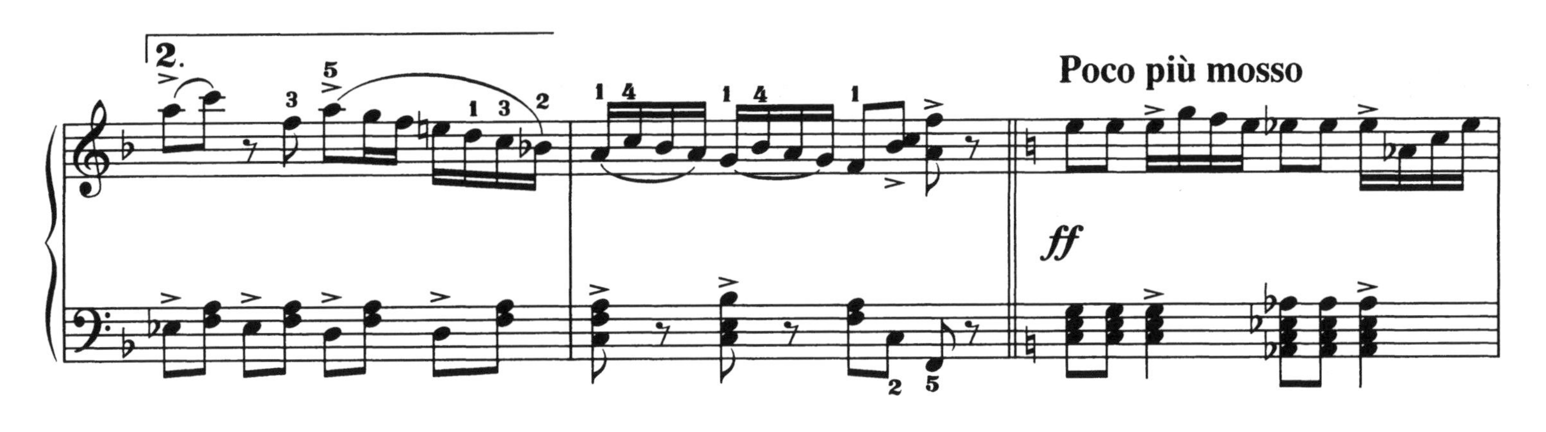
2.
Poco più mosso
ff

Ped.
Ped.

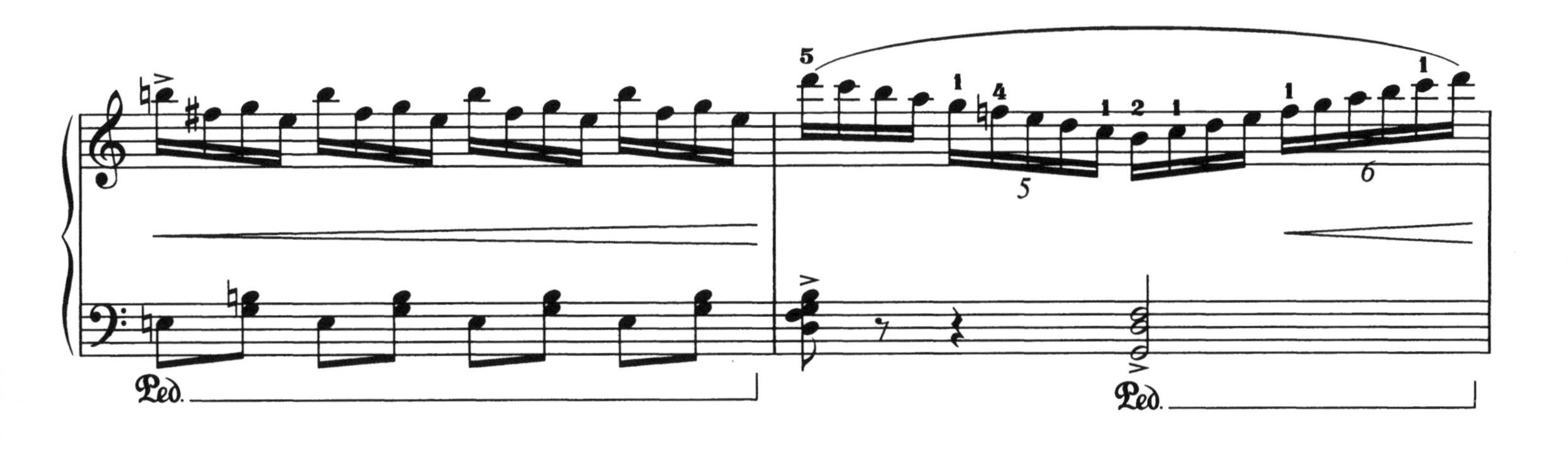
Ped.
Ped.

Più mosso
fff
6

Ped.
Ped.
Ped.
Ped.
Ped.
Furioso
Ped.
Ped.
Ped.
Ped.
Ped.
sf
8va
Ped.

A Japanese Carnival

mf
ff
ff
Ped.
(Cymbal)

ff
Ped.
Ped.
Poco meno mosso
p
dolce

Like two Piccolos
8va
(8)

rit.
(Cymbal)
Broadly
ff
con Ped.
a tempo
mf

ff
Ped.
ff
Ped.

5
3
2
1
5
4
8ves ad lib.
8va
(8)
sf
8va
Ped.
a tempo
(8)
1
1
1
Ped.
(8)
Ped.
Ped.
8va

By The Blue Hawaiian Waters

Tone-Picture

Composer's synopsis

After a short dreamy introduction, a vigorous movement illustrates the well-known Hawaiian "Hula Dance"; this is succeeded by a misterioso passage representing the arrival of the native (or "Kanaka") lover; he plays his native love-call; this leads into the "Song of the Hula Girl"; it gradually dies away and is succeeded by the "Dance of the Betrothal Ceremony", which brings the piece to a lively conclusion.

Introduction

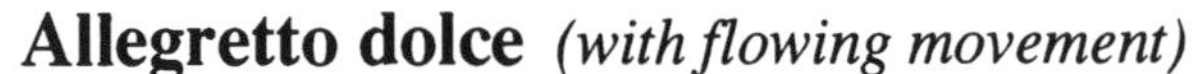

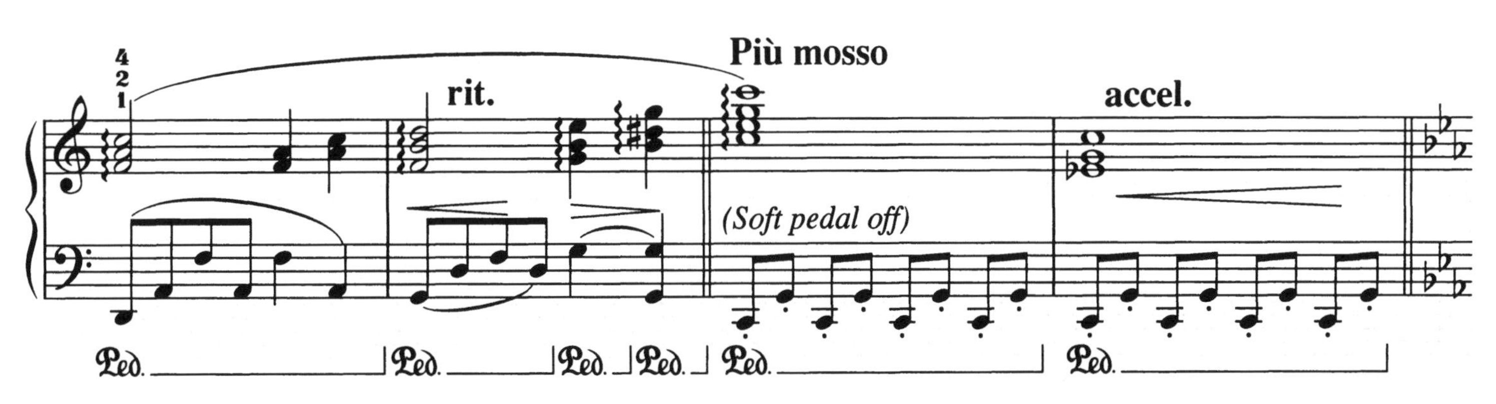

*The grace-notes may be omitted.

The "Hula" Dance
Allegro vigoroso
sempre stacc.
8va

8va
ff
Ped.
Ped.
Ped.
Ped.

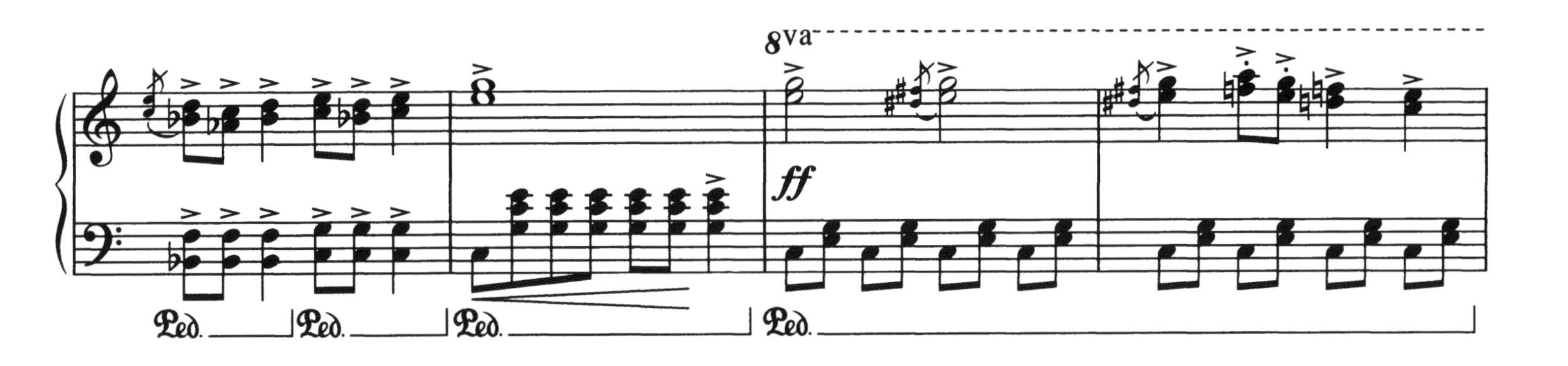
8va
ff
Ped.
Ped.
Ped.
Ped.

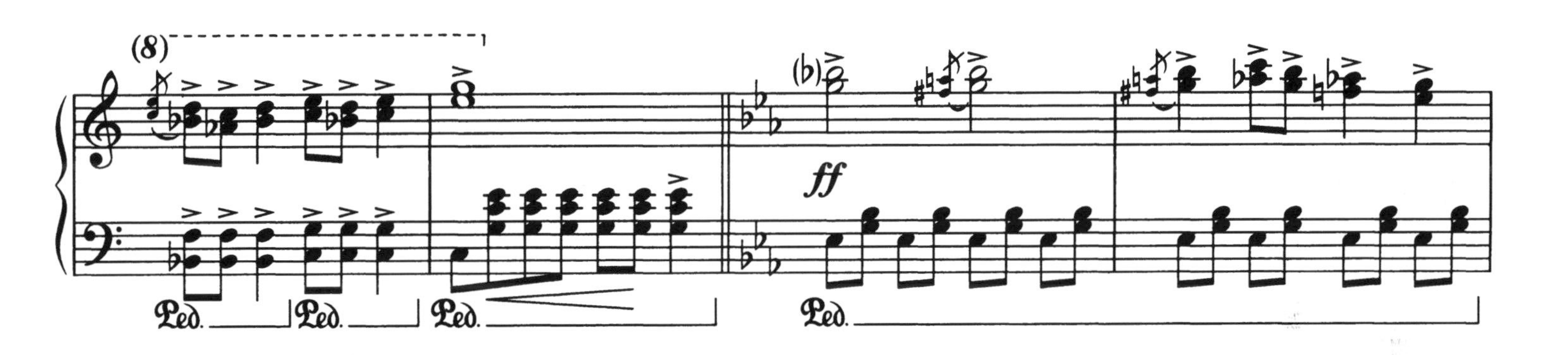
(8)
ff
Ped.
Ped.
Ped.
Ped.

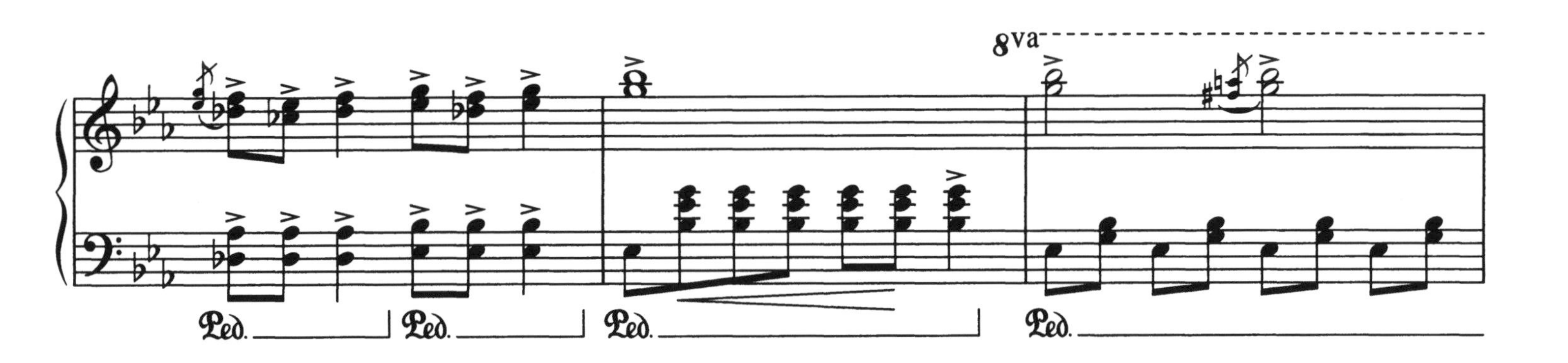
8va
Ped.
Ped.
Ped.
Ped.

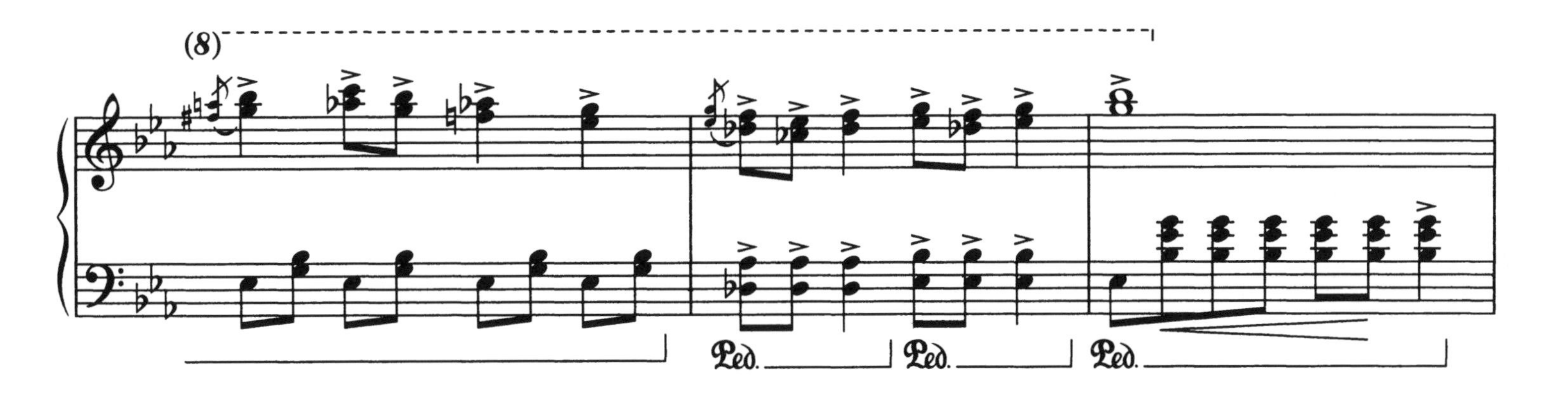
(8)
Ped.
Ped.
Ped.

ff
Ped.
sf
The "Kanaka" Lover appears
Moderato misterioso
p
8va

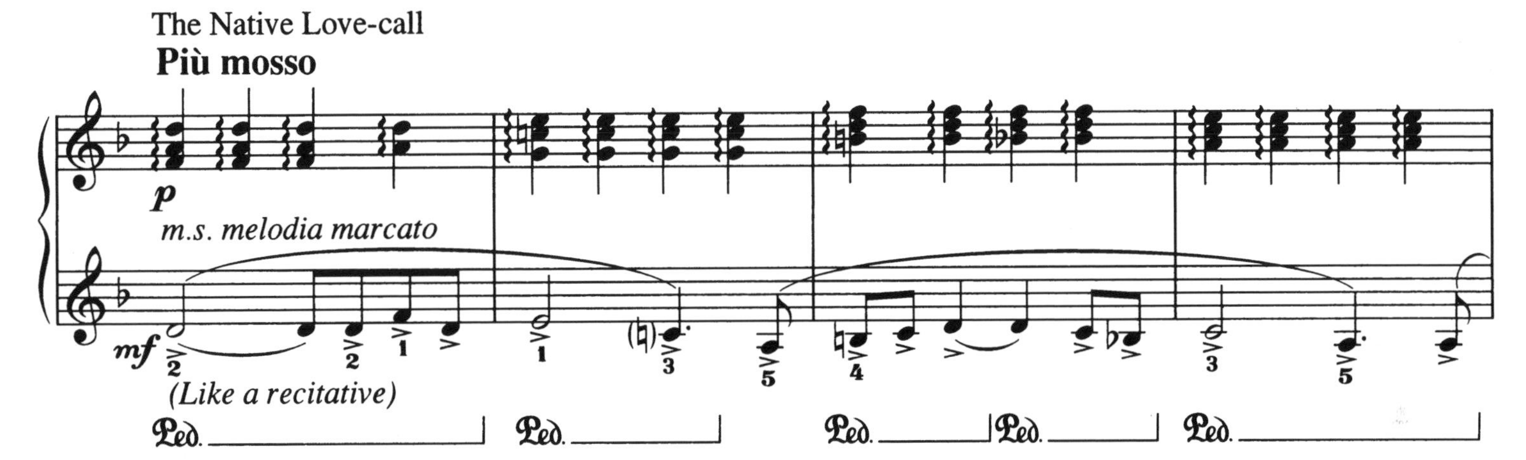

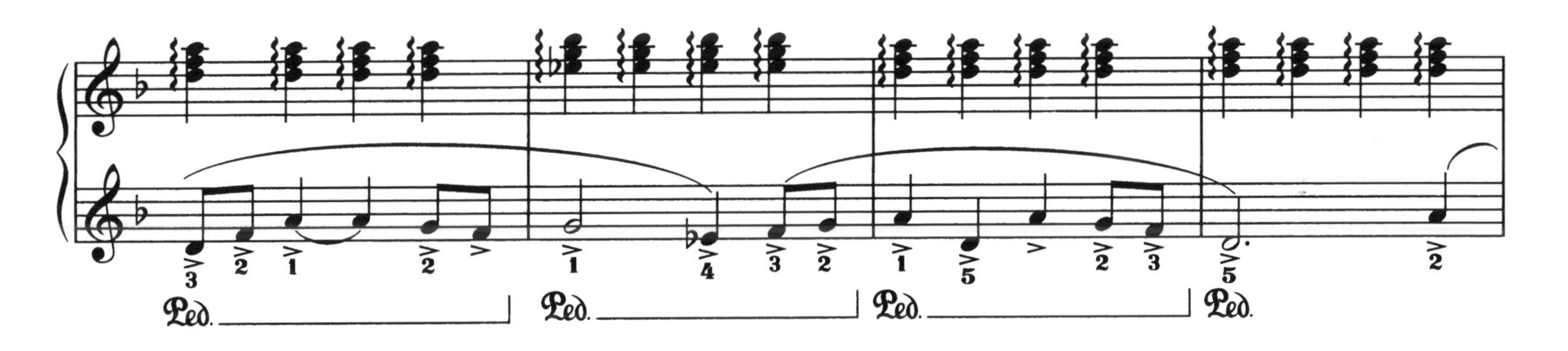

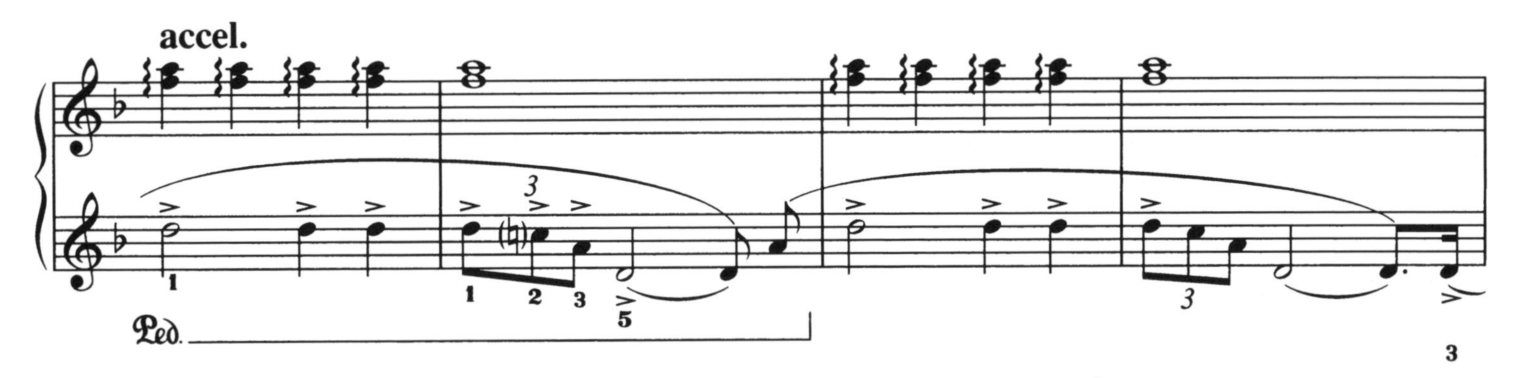

A cut to the next ⊕ may be made here if desired

The song of the "Hula" Girl

Allegretto espressivo *(with a flowing movement)*

*The grace-notes may be omitted.

*The grace-notes may be omitted.

*The grace-notes may be omitted.

Dance of the Betrothal Ceremony

Vivace spiritoso

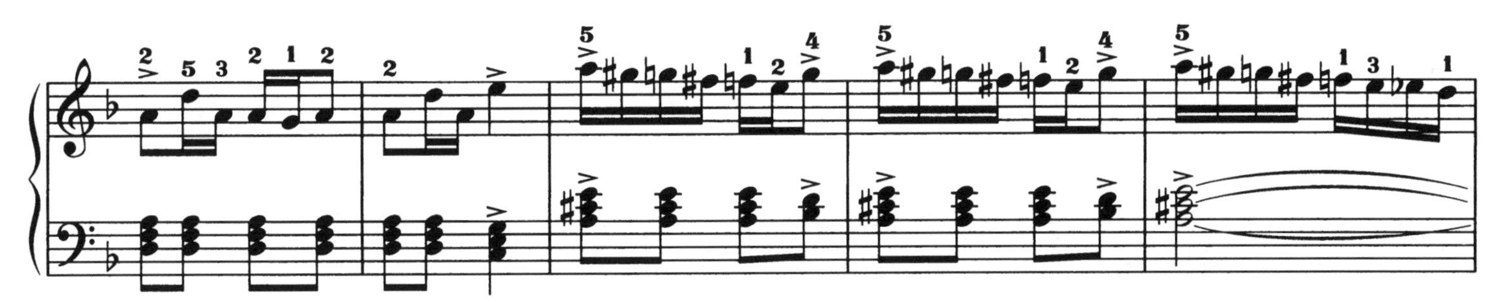

*The grace-notes may be omitted.

ff
Ped.
ff
f

8va
f
ff

*The grace-notes may be omitted.

The Clock And The Dresden Figures

Composer's synopsis

Two Dresden-china figures standing on each side of a clock come to life and dance to the ticking of the clock; after a while the clock goes wrong, the spring breaks and the two figures rush back to their former positions.

Con moto (♩ = about 120)

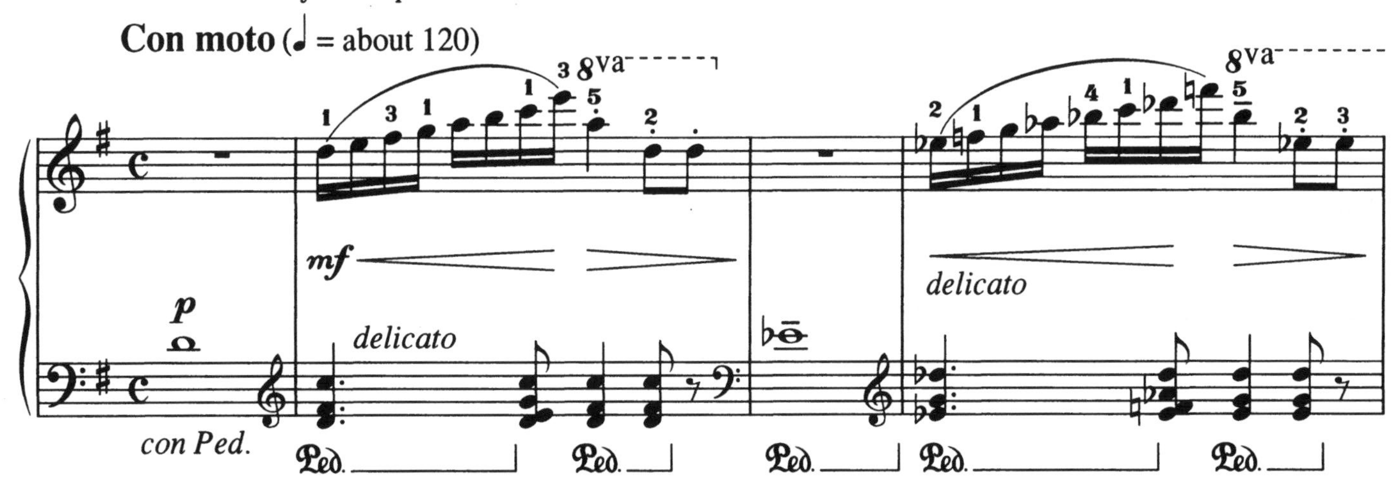

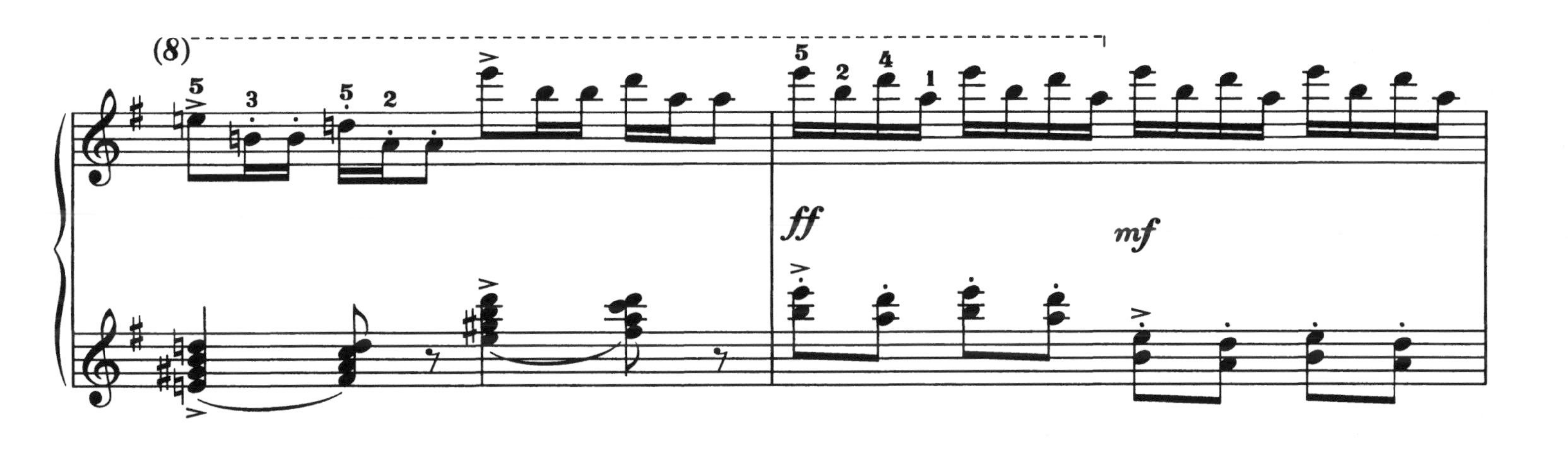

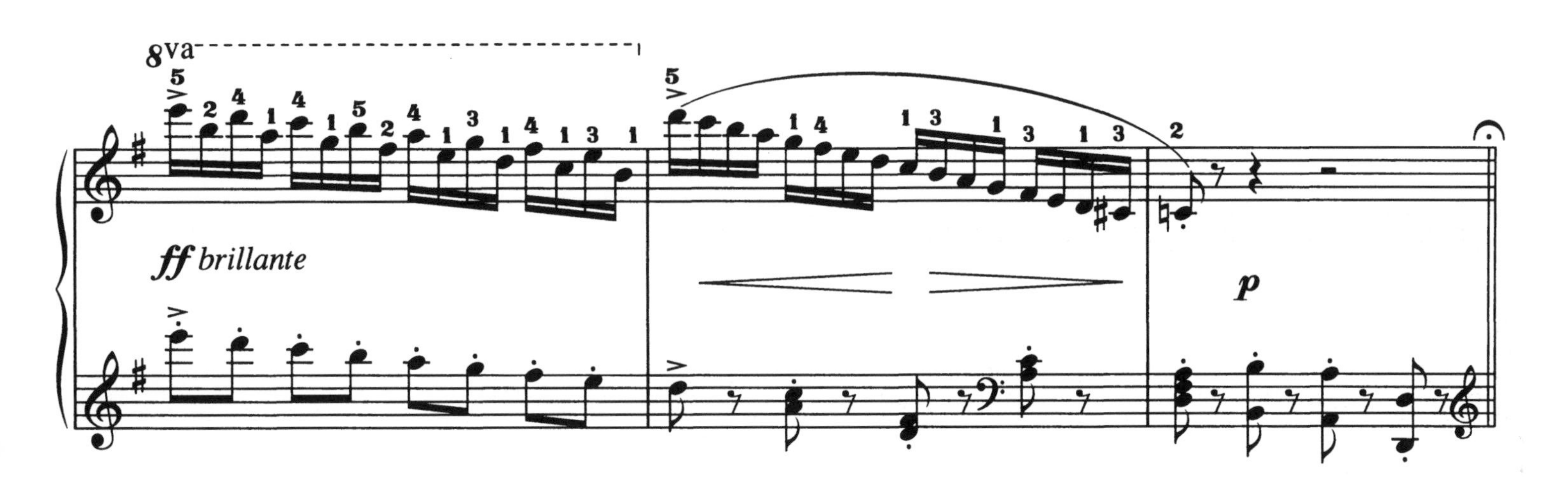

8va
The Clock ticks
p
p stacc. leggiero

(8)

(8)

mf
poco marcato

5
3
2
8va
(8)
f
The clock strikes
8va
daintily
con Ped.
Ossia:
(8)

(8)
(8)
f
f
8va
p leggiero e delicato
(8)
marcato

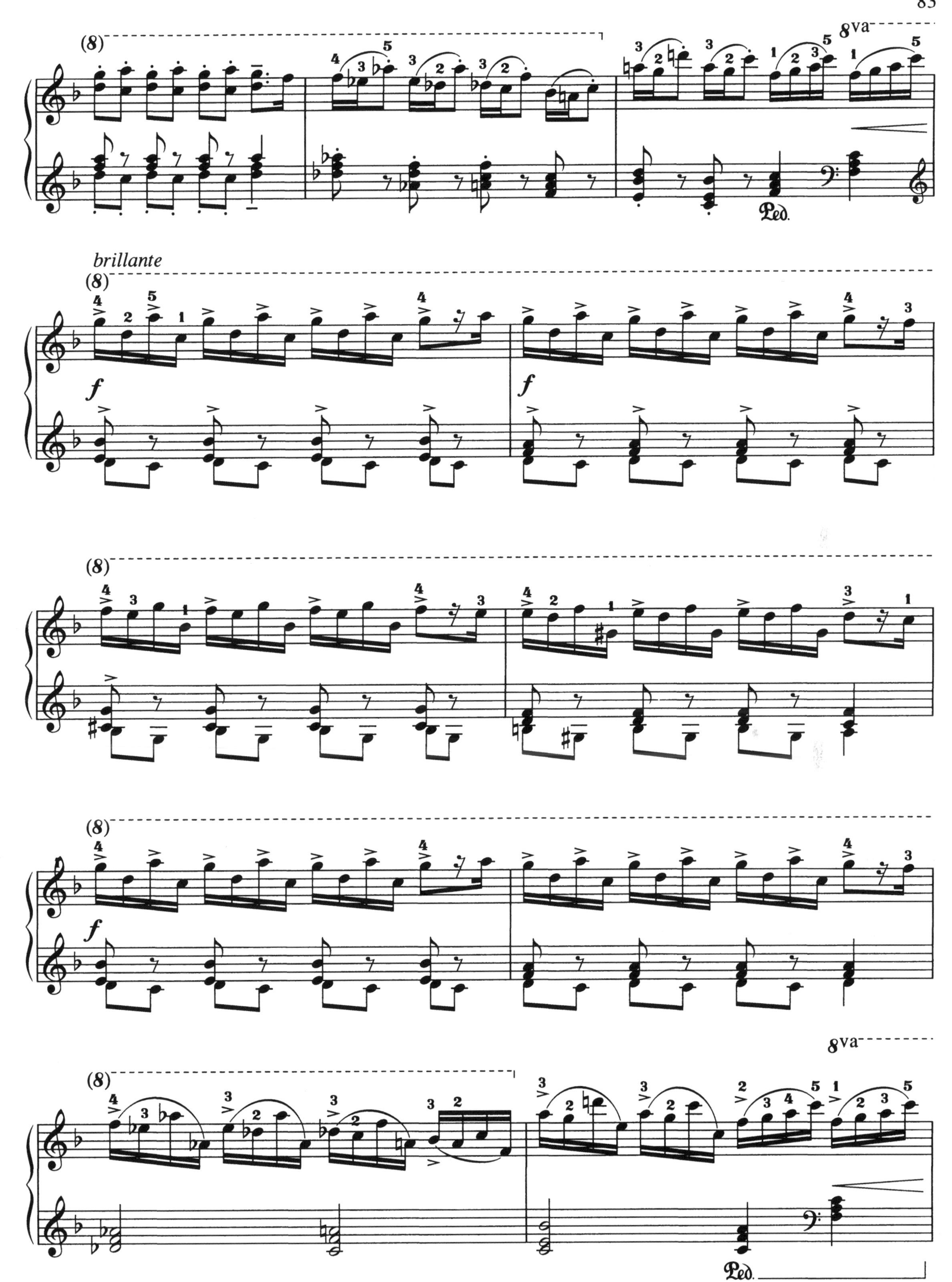
(8)
8va
brillante
(8)
f
f
(8)
(8)
f
(8)
8va
Ped.
Ped.

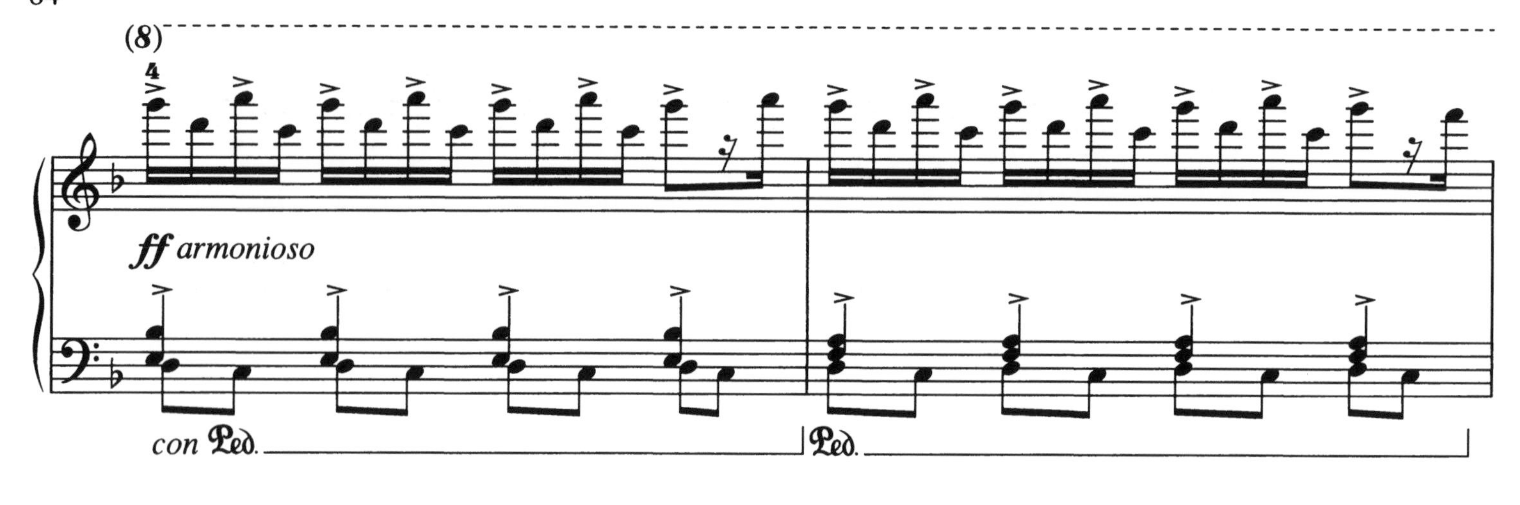
(8)
ff armonioso
con Ped.
Ped.

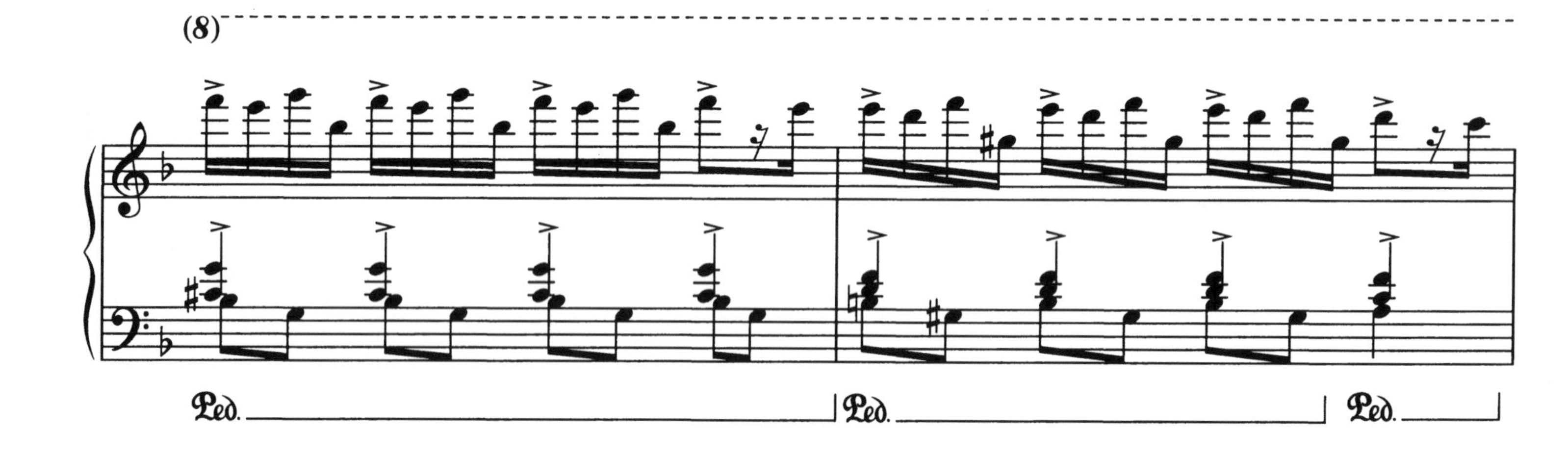
(8)
Ped.
Ped.
Ped.

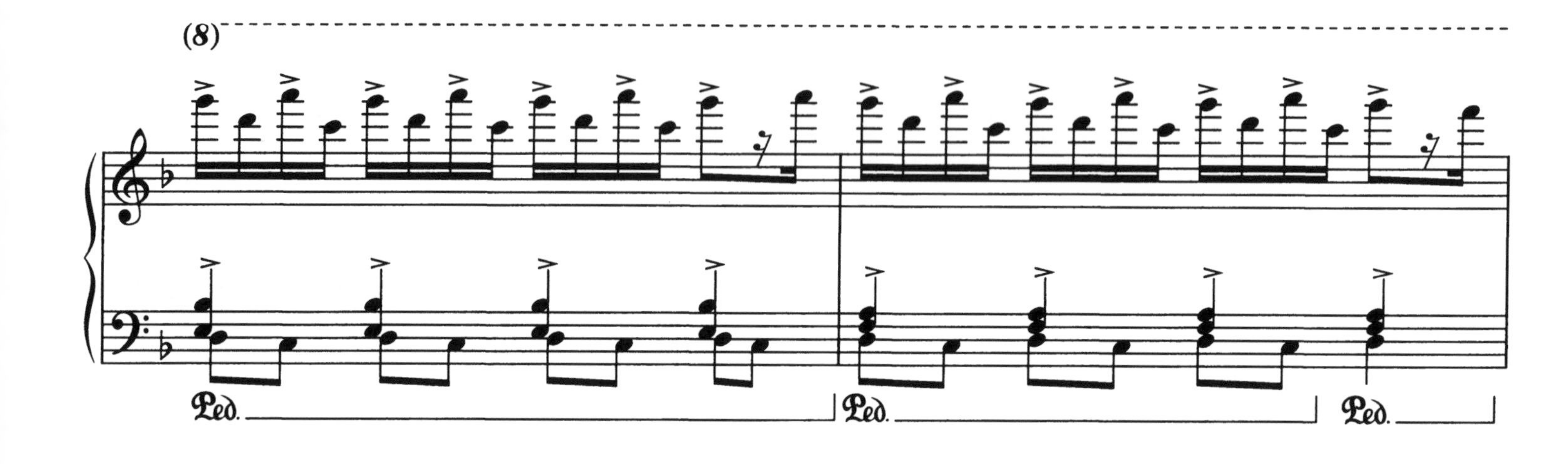
(8)
Ped.
Ped.
Ped.

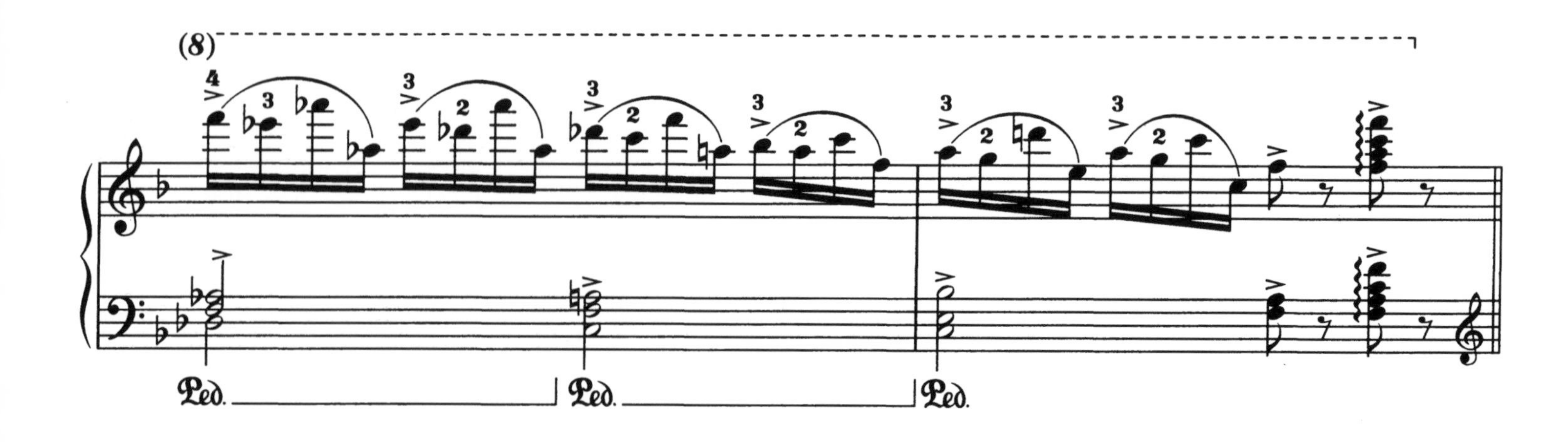
(8)
Ped.
Ped.
Ped.

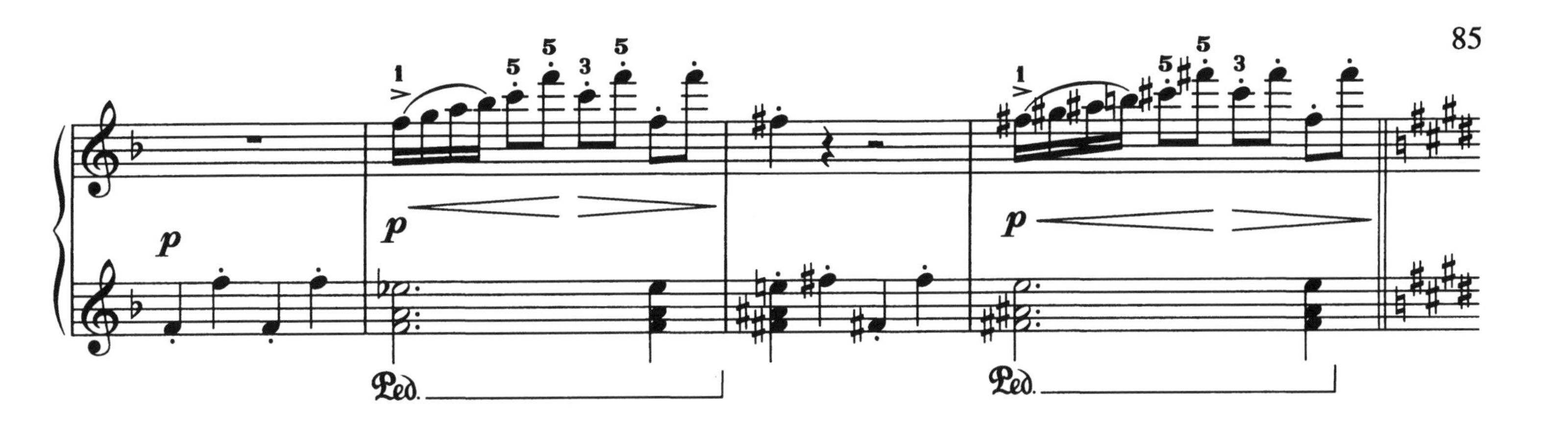
p
p
Ped.
p
Ped.

8va
delicato
dim.
pp with soft Pedal
Ped.

(8)

(8)

tre corde
marcato
8va
(8)
f
f
daintily
con Ped.

(8)
(8)
(8)
(8)
f brillante

(8)
(8)
(8)
8va
Ped.
(8)
ff armonioso
con Ped.
Ped.
(8)
Ped.
Ped.
Ped.
(8)
Ped.
Ped.
Ped.

The clock goes wrong
accel.
The clock spring breaks
a tempo
Vivace
facilité
sff
ff brillante
fff
sf

Fairies Of The Stream

Valse Brillante

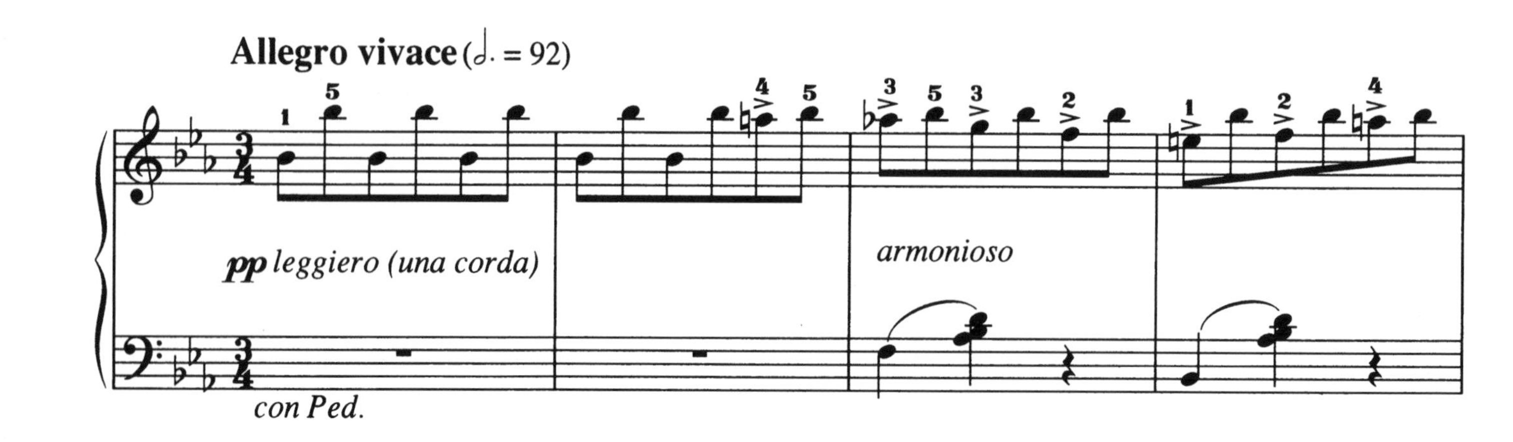

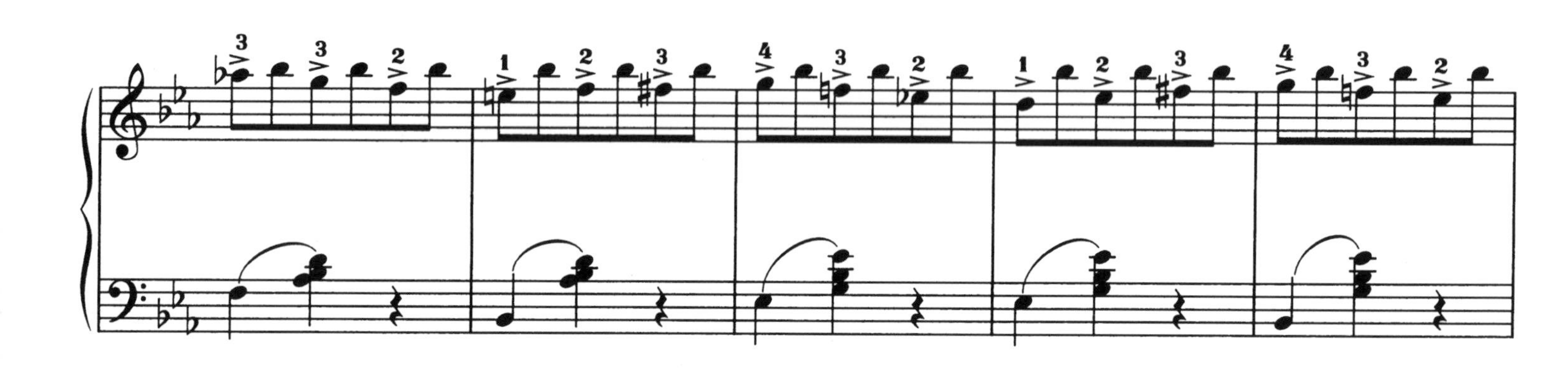

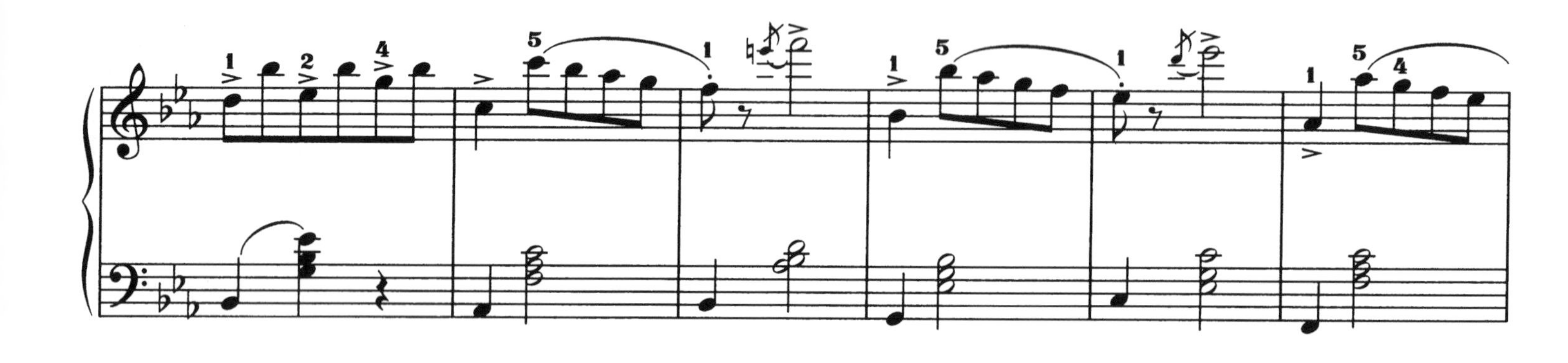

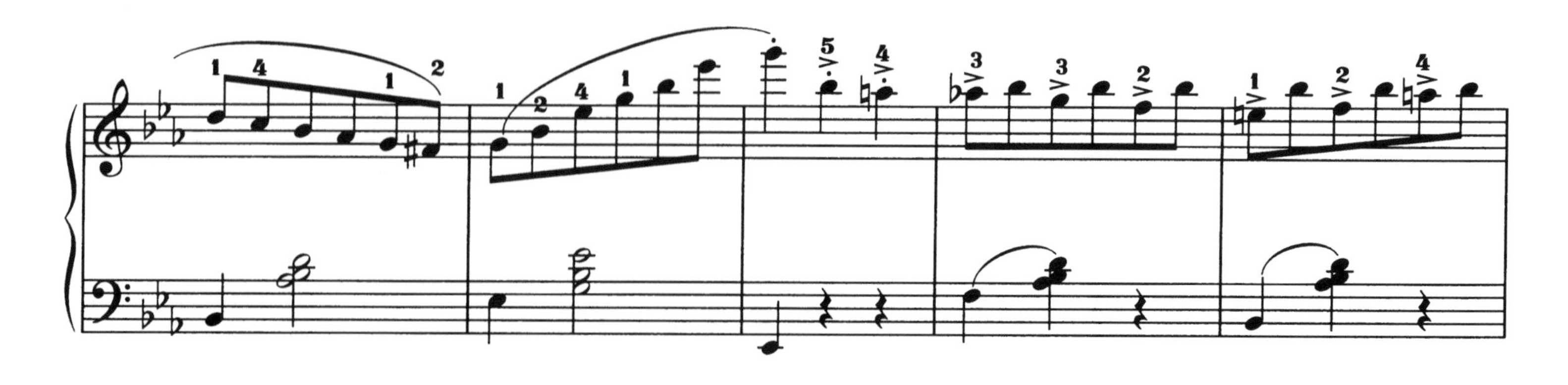

8va
f (tre corde)

8va
(8)
cresc. molto
(8)
ff brillante
(8)
sf
ff brillante
Ped.

8va
Ped.

rit.
repeat R.H. 8va
mf
p grazioso
3
5
rit.
sostenuto
a tempo
cresc.
Ped.
Ped.
Ped.

Ped.
pp
(una corda)

8va
ff brillante
L.H. pesante

accel. al Fine
ff brillante
8
con 8va
con 8va
Ped.

Jungle Drums

Patrol

Composer's synopsis

Drums of different sizes play an important part in native ceremonies, and tribes are said to be able to converse secretly with each other by means of the "drum-language." The drums are beaten by hand as well as with sticks, and during the incessant drumming other natives drone a sort of dirge.

* To imitate the Tom-Tom strike the lid of the Piano softly with the knuckles of R.H. in the rhythm indicated.

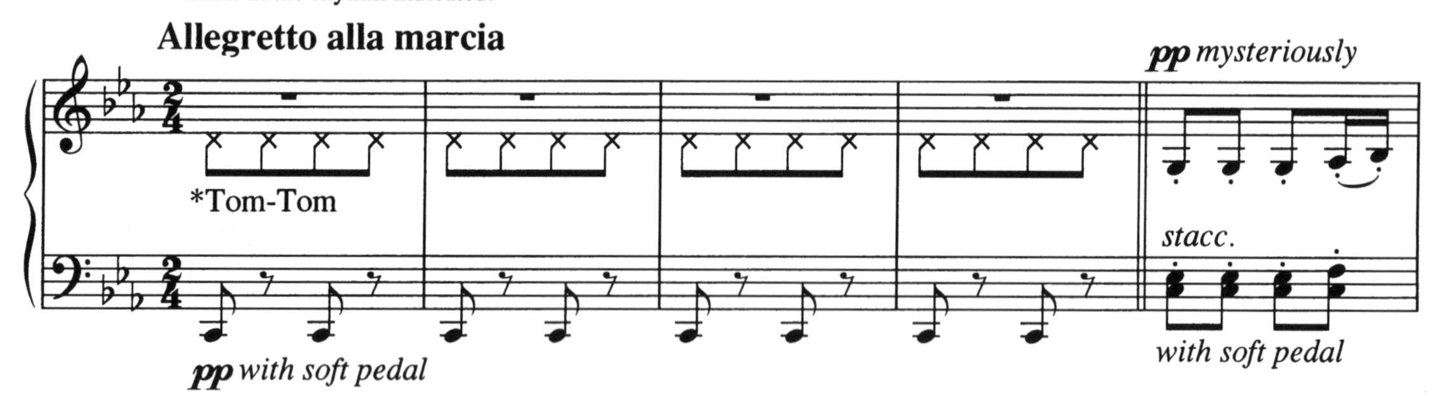

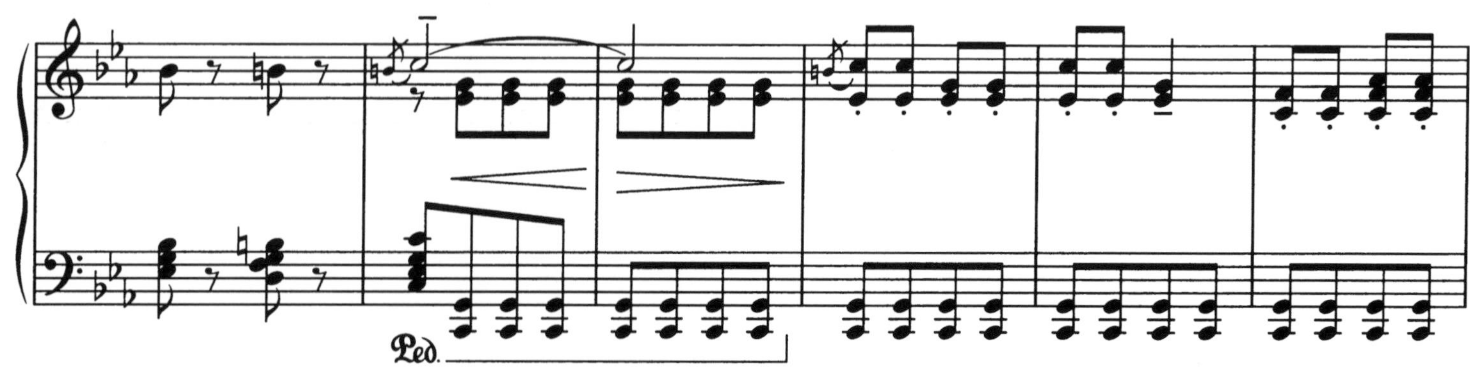

cresc.
poco - - a - poco
mf tre corde
marcato
basso
8ves ad lib.
Ped.
8va
cresc.
marcato
Ped.

*The lower notes of 3rds in R.H. may be omitted.

1.
2.
basso marcato
ff
Ped.

sf
sf
sf
sf
Ped.
Ped.
simile
Ped.
(Brass)
8va
ff
Ped.
Ped.
Ped.
Ped.
(8)
Ped.
Ped.
Ped.
Ped.
Ped.
Ped.
Ped.
(8)
sf
sf
sf
sf
Ped.
Ped.
simile
Ped.

fff sing loudly
Ah ah ah ah ah ah
ff
fff
ah
Ah
Like drums
Ah
R.H.
sf
Ah ah ah ah ah ah ah
Ah

Ah ah ah ah ah ah ah
Ah
Ah
R.H.
sf
Ped.
Ah ah ah ah ah ah ah
Ah
fff
basso marcato

sf
Ped.

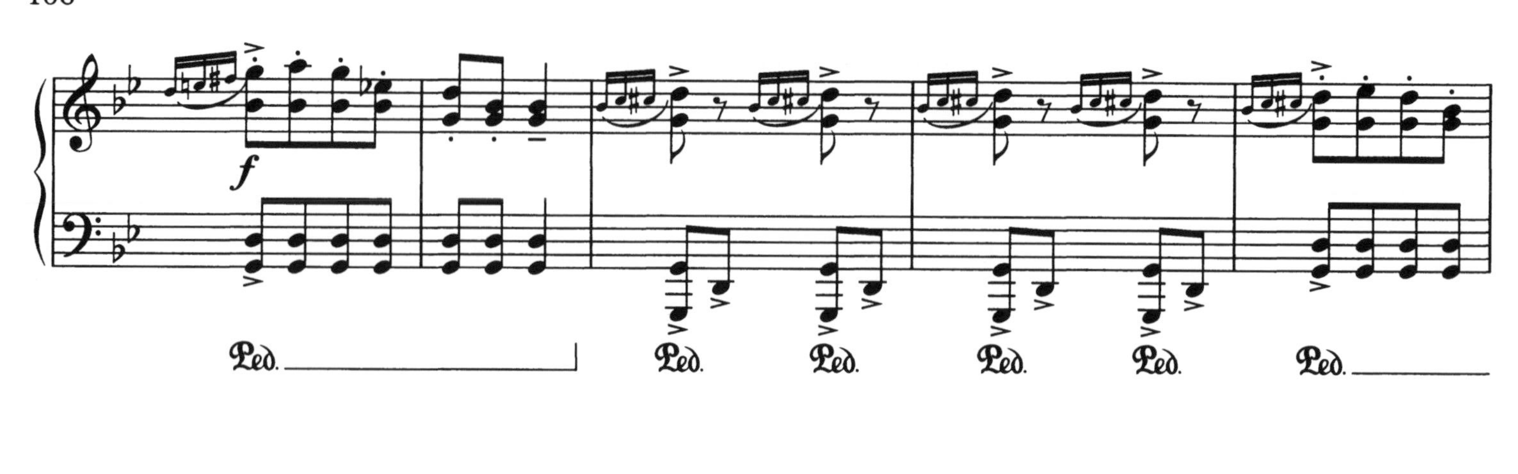

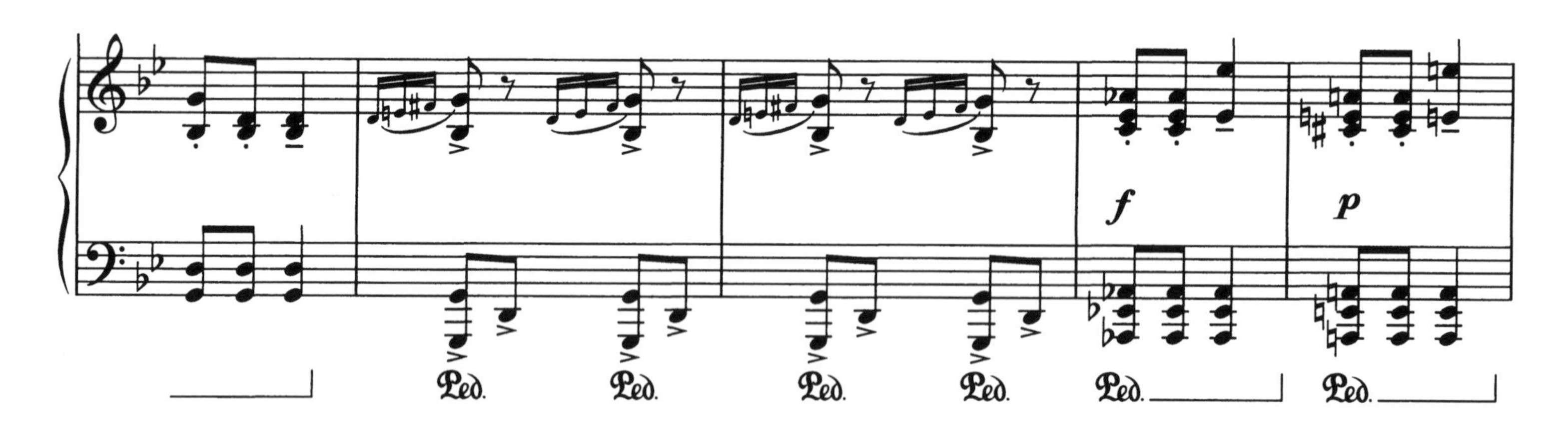

*The lower notes of 3rds in R.H. may be omitted.

Ped.
Ped.
Ped.
p
leggiero
p
dim.
p
sonore
Ped.
Ped.
Ped.
Ped.
Ped.
Ped.
Ped.
Ped.
Ped.

Ped.

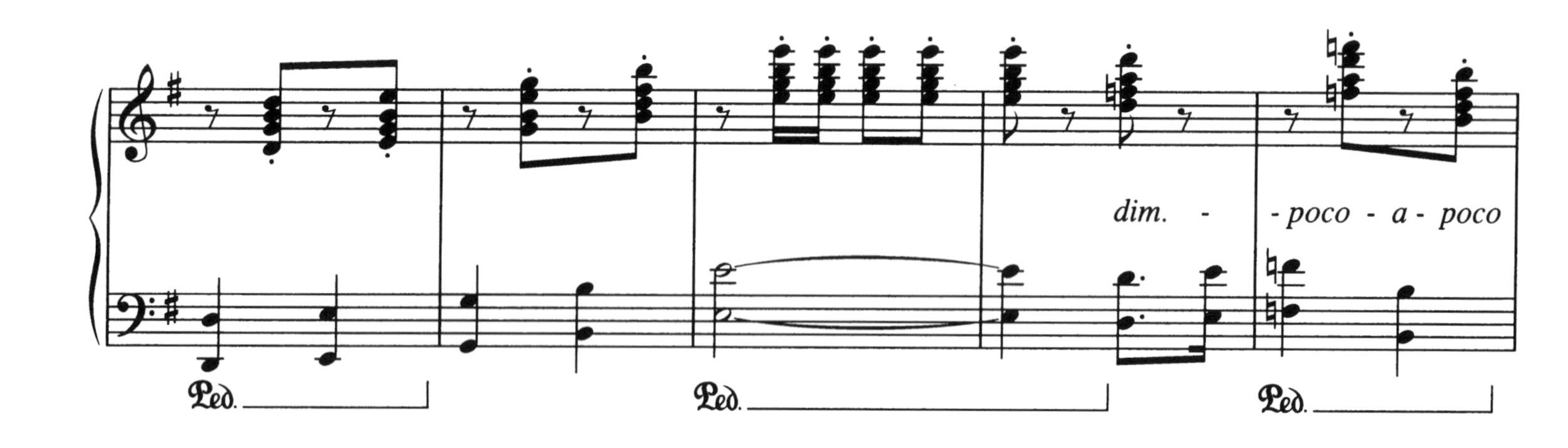
dim. - - poco - a - poco
Ped.
Ped.
Ped.

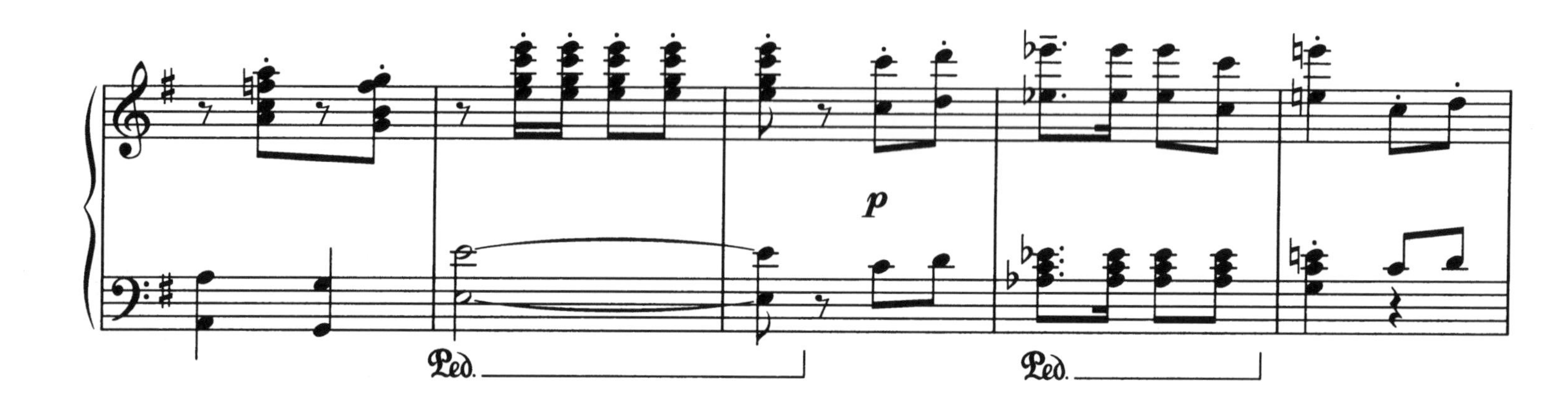
p
Ped.
Ped.

dim. - poco - a - poco
p
Ped.
Ped.
Ped.

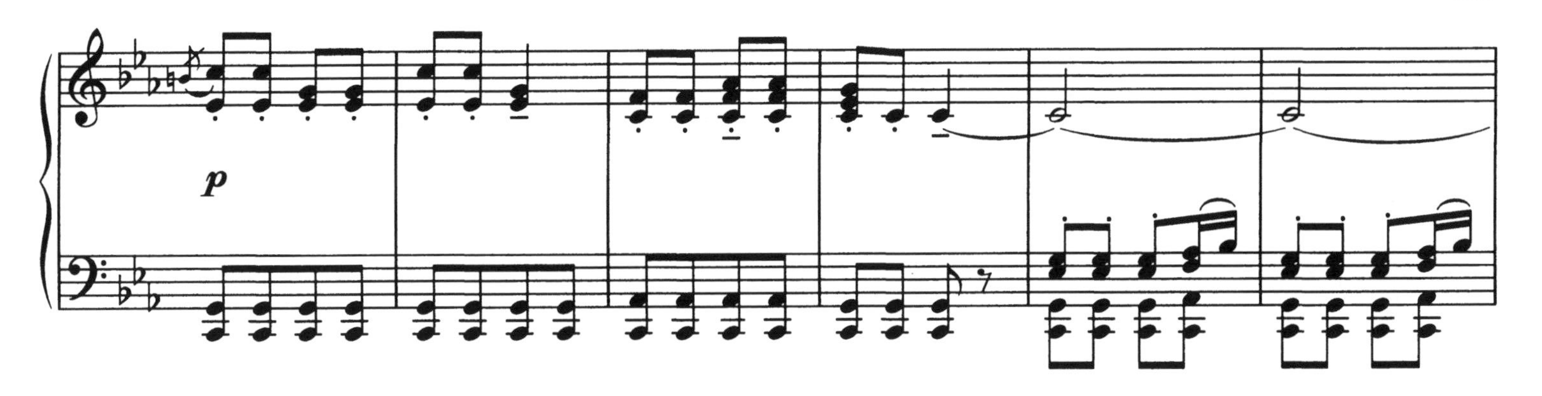
p

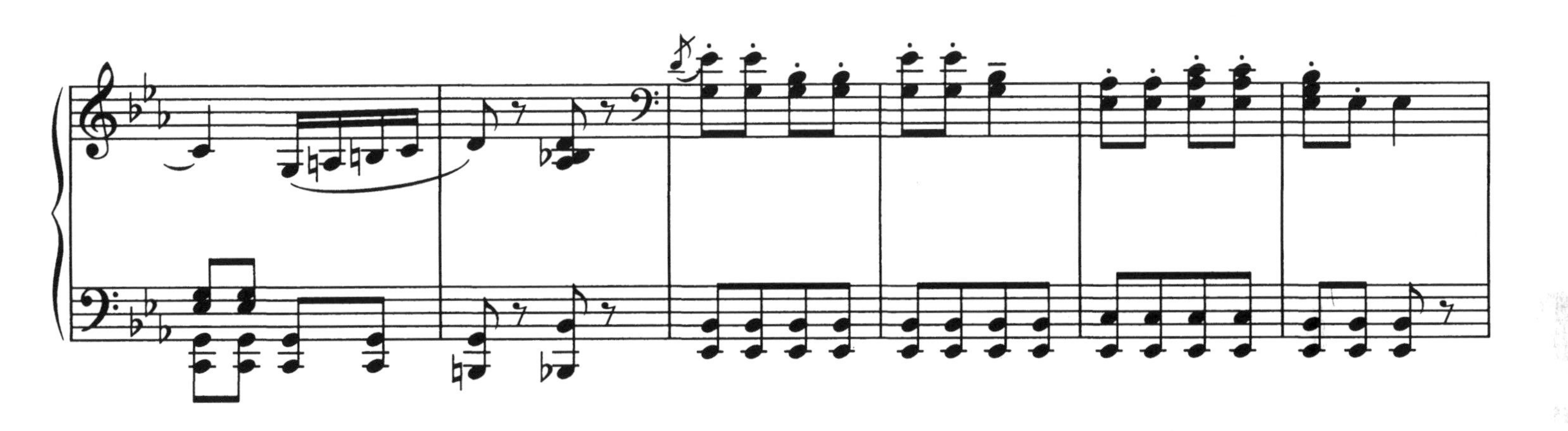

pp

with soft Pedal
poco - - a - - - poco - - dim.
morendo
ppp
8

Love And The Dancer

Intermezzo

Composer's synopsis

This piece represents a young man who has fallen in love with a girl who dances at the theatre. The first theme portrays the young man's ardent feelings, and the second theme represents the ballet in which the girl is dancing. The first theme is now repeated in the celeste, as if the girl were dancing to it; then the full orchestra takes it up appassionato, gradually dying down as the curtain falls.

mf
con Ped.
f sostenuto
con Ped.
Ped.
sostenuto
con Ped.
espress.
pp
Ped.

Poco più mosso

rit.
a tempo
ten.
ten.
mf
Ped.
Ped.
marcato
con Ped.
Tempo I
rit.
a tempo
8va
p
p (a la Celeste)
Ped.
(8)
loco
Ped.

sostenuto
f
Ped.
con Ped.
f
p
con Ped.
L.H.
p
mf marcato
melodia
rit.
Ped.

Italian Twilight

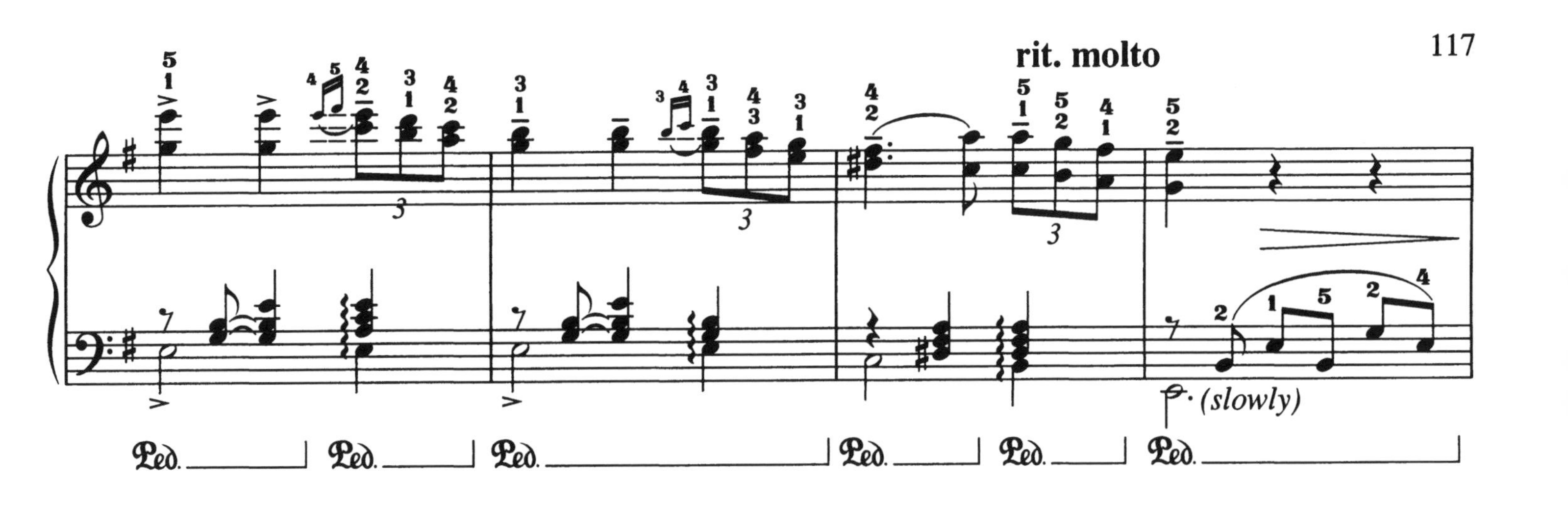
rit. molto
(slowly)
Ped.

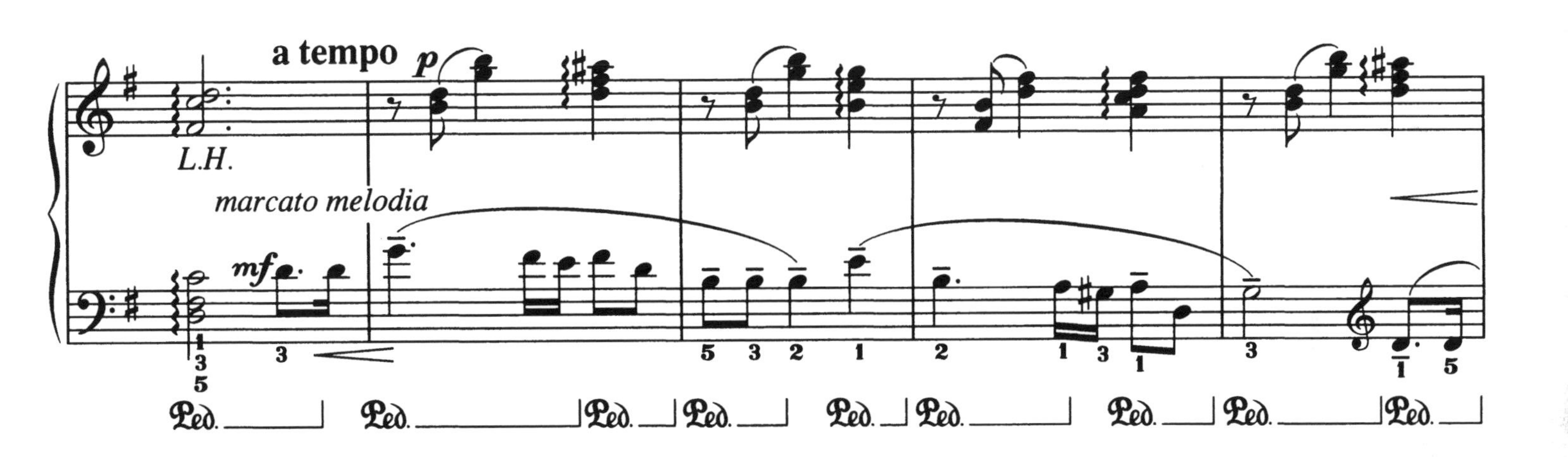
a tempo
L.H.
marcato melodia
Ped.

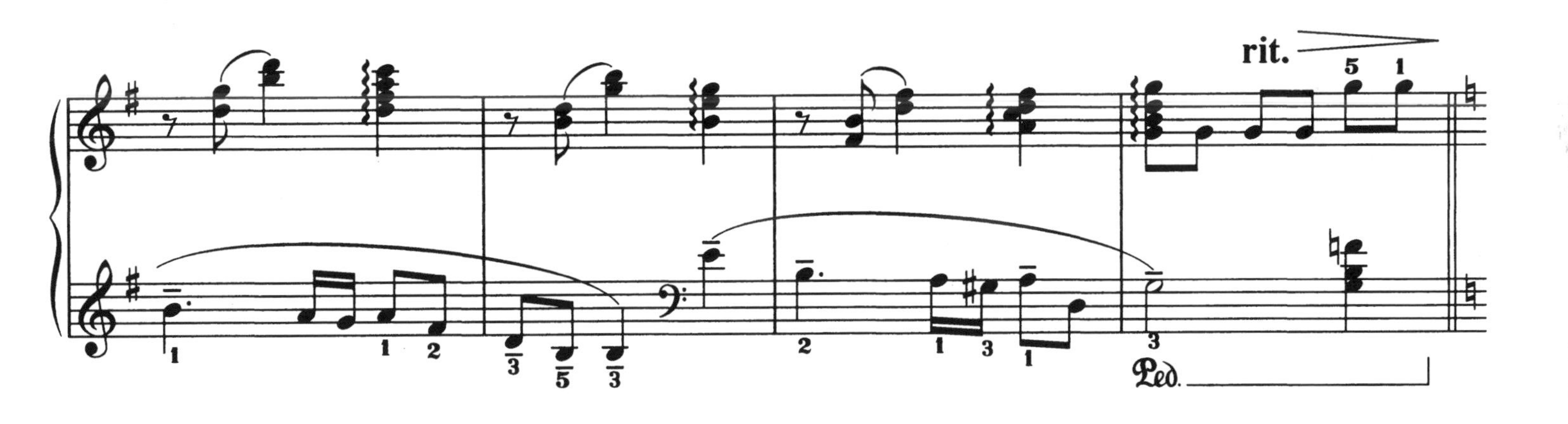
rit.
Ped.

a tempo
pastorale
Evening Bell
Ped.

mf
marcato
f
mf
L.H.
marcato
allargando
f
mf
dolce
rall.
8va
pp
pp
Tempo I (do not hurry)
mf
marcato
quasi arpa
marcato espressivo with
soft pedal

marcato delicato
mf
sostenuto
(Bell)
Ped.
mf
marcato
allargando
p
marcato
rit. molto
a tempo
poco a poco rall.
8va
pp

In The Moonlight

Poetic Intermezzo

Più mosso
mf sonore
con Ped.
rit.
Tempo I
p delicato
Ped.
simile

Ped.
Ped.
Ped.

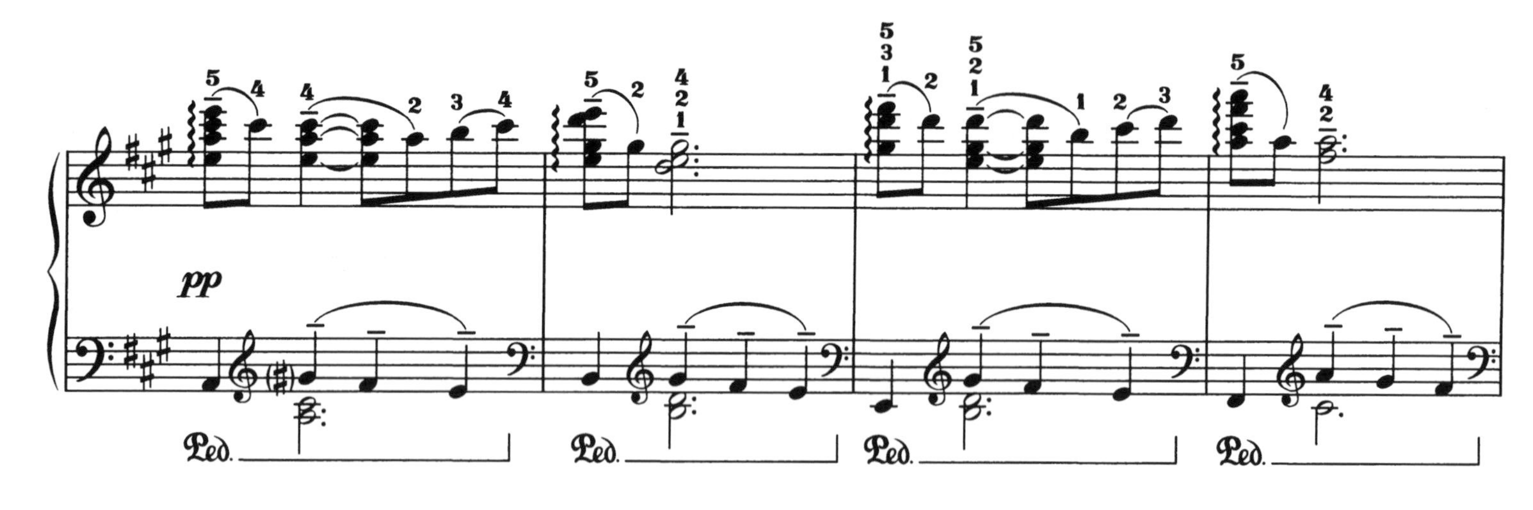
pp
Ped.
Ped.
Ped.
Ped.

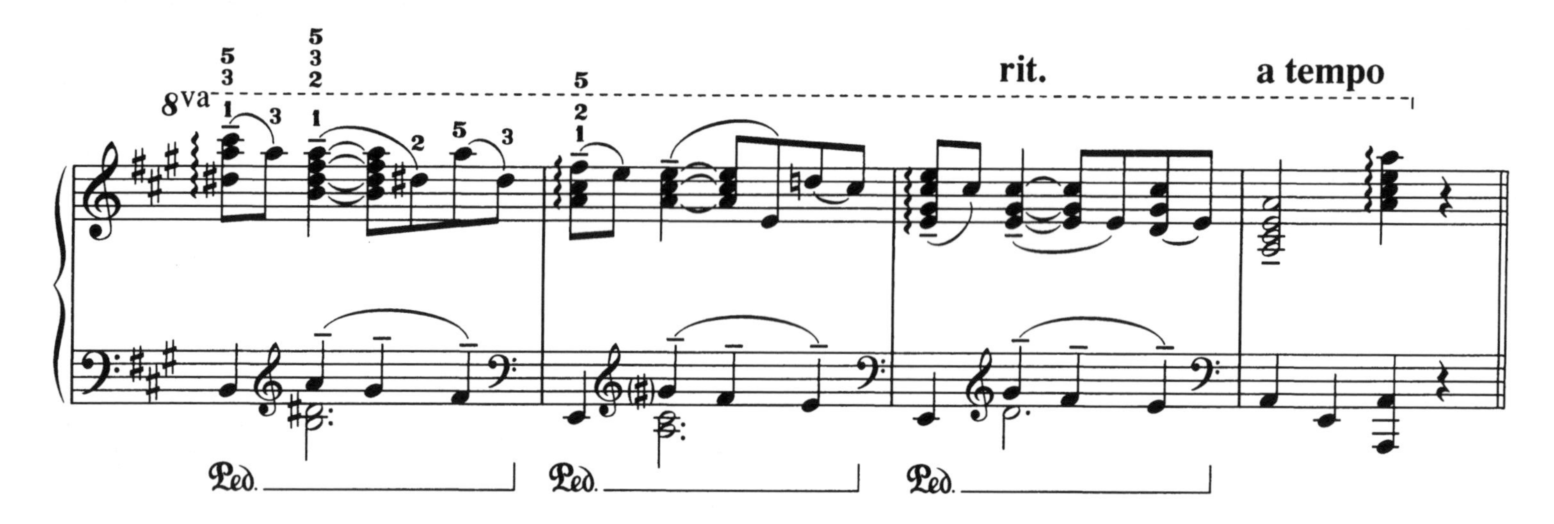
8va
rit.
a tempo
Ped.
Ped.
Ped.

Più mosso, Appassionato (tempo rubato)

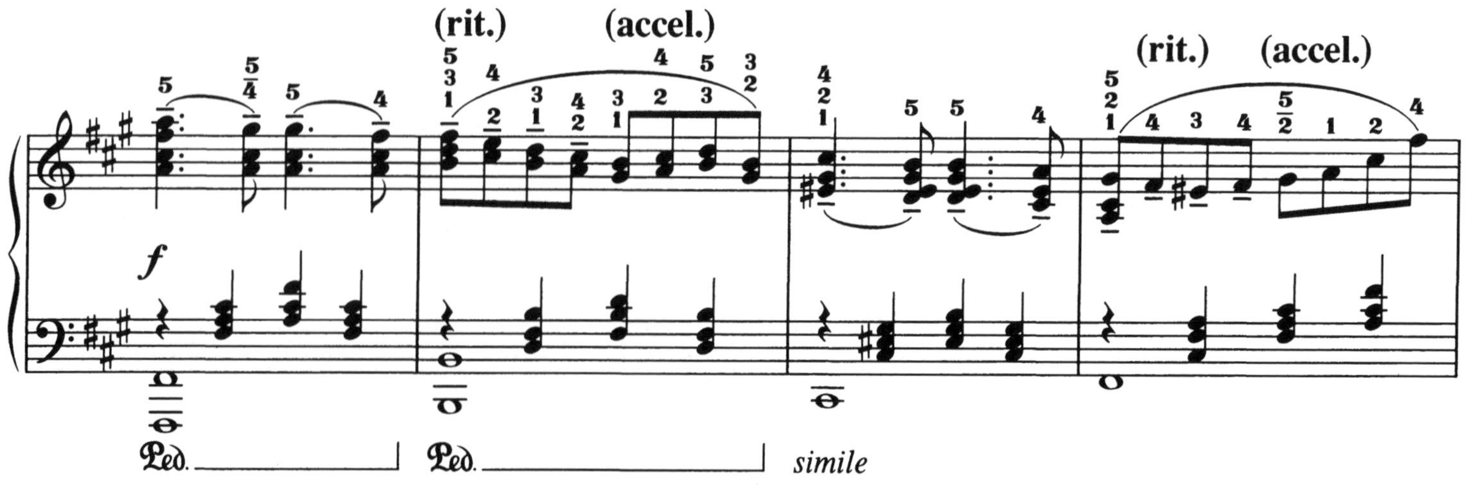
(rit.)
(accel.)
(rit.)
(accel.)
f
Ped.
Ped.
simile

accel. poco a poco
rubato
rit.
ff
p
Ped.
a tempo
(rit.)
(accel.)
f
simile
rit.
Tempo I
p delicato

pp
8va
rit.
a tempo
Più mosso
p
rall.
accel.
8va
pp

Wedgwood Blue

A Dance

mf

Ped.
Ped.
Ped.
Ped.
Ped.
Ped.
Ped.
8va

p delicato
mf espressivo
Ped.
Ped.
Ped.

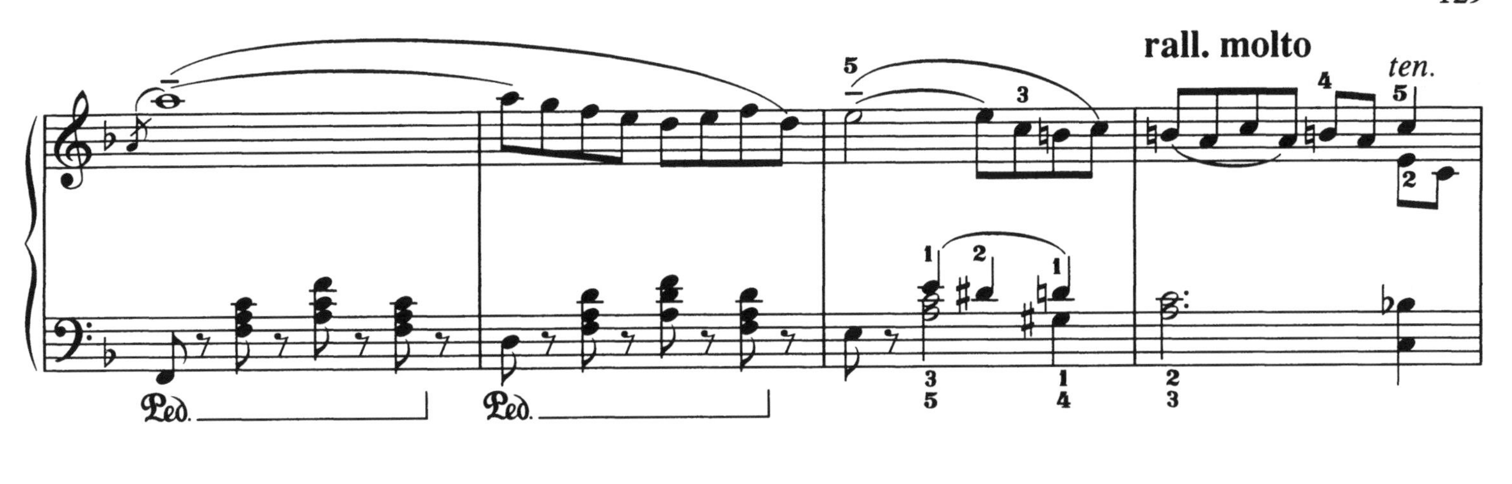
rall. molto
ten.

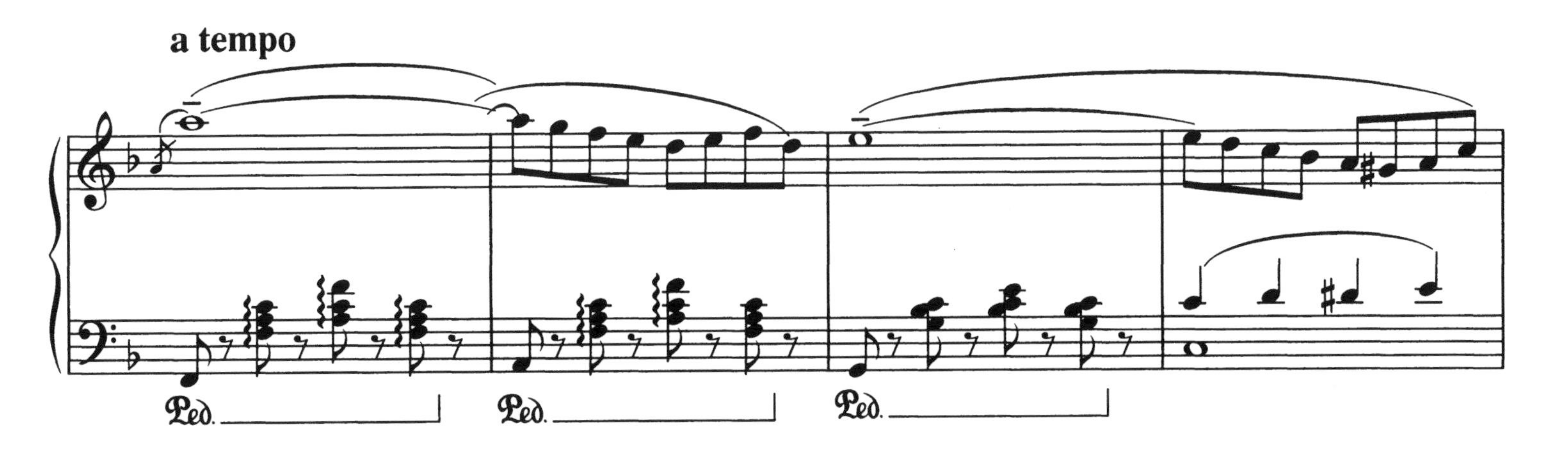
a tempo

rall.
a tempo
repeat ad lib.

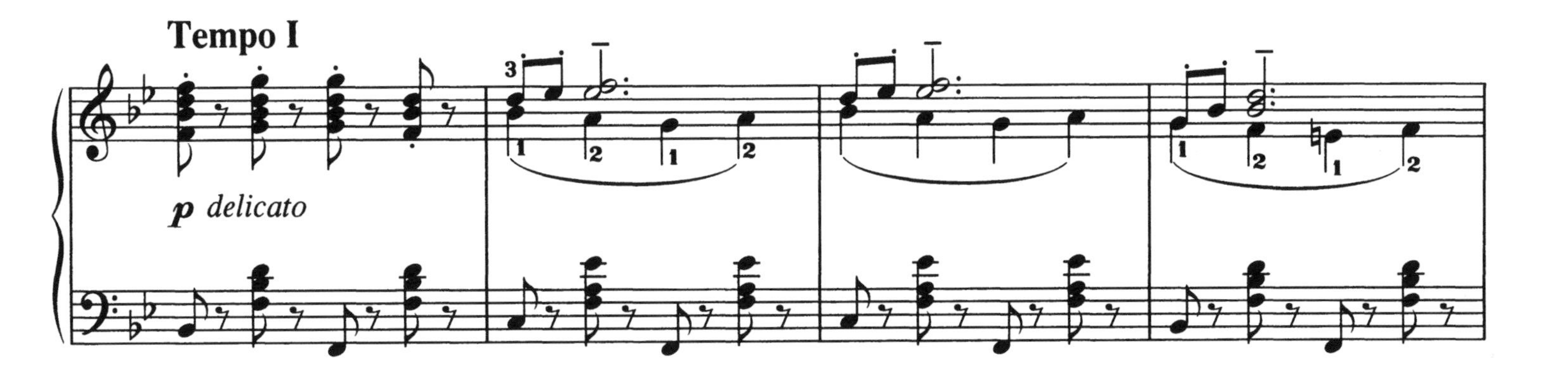
Tempo I
p delicato

8va ad lib.
(8)
5
3
1
5
4
1
mf
rall.
a tempo
8va
p

Gallantry
Duo d'amour
Intermezzo–Romance

Composer's synopsis

The piece opens with a cello solo (with piano accompaniment), representing the man's declaration of love, followed by a violin solo representing the lady. The two themes are then played together simultaneously, hence the sub-title "Duo d'amour". After an episode of passionate character, the original themes are played by the full orchestra, the piece ending quietly and serenely.

*The R.H. accompaniment must be very light and very soft.

a tempo
mf espress.
sostenuto
Ped.
tre corde
Ped.
rit.
rall.
Ped.
Duetto (both melodies well marked)
p sostenuto e dolce
Ped.
Ped.

mf
rall. e dim.
f
pp
Poco più mosso
(rit.)
(a tempo)
f appassionato
con Ped.
(rit.)
allarg.

ff con passione
Ped.
Ped.
Ped.
Ped.
allarg.
(rit.)
(rit.)
(rit.)
mf
p espress.
a tempo
ad lib. 8va
ff
(8)
ten.
rall.
fff
p subito
pp
Tempo I
pp
3 2 1 2 1 2
1 2
1
3 1
2 1
mf molto espress.
with both pedals

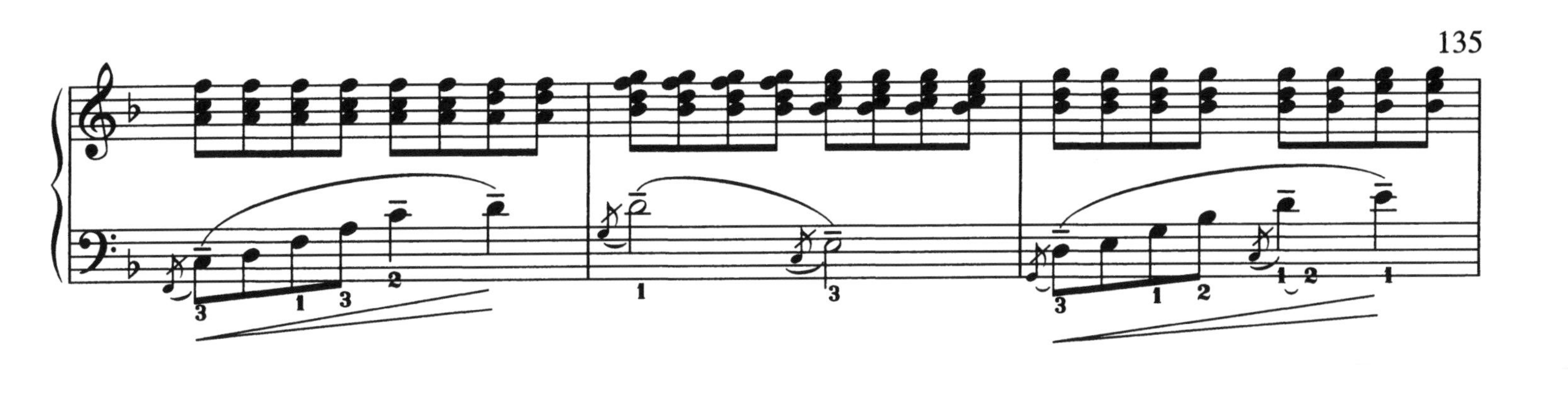

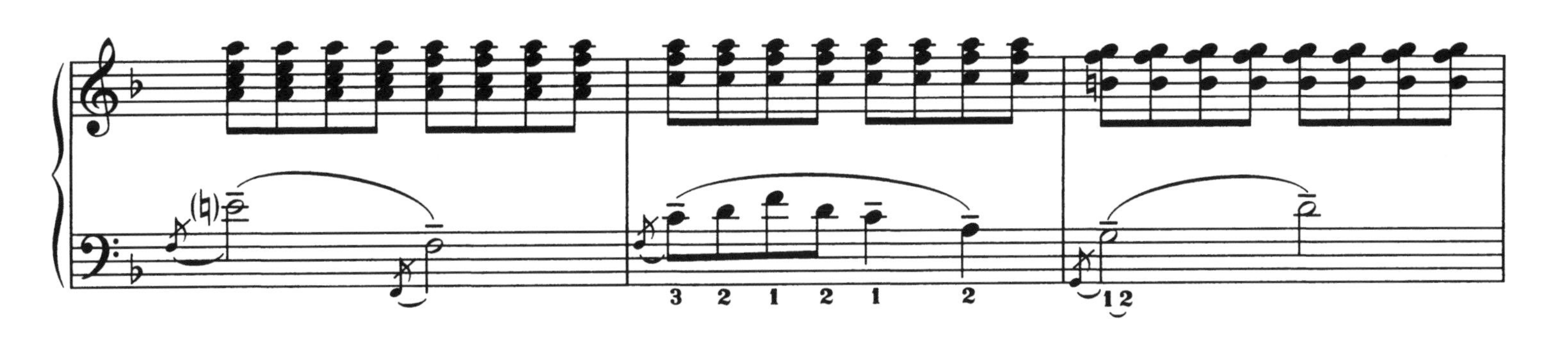

8va
rall.
f
tre corde

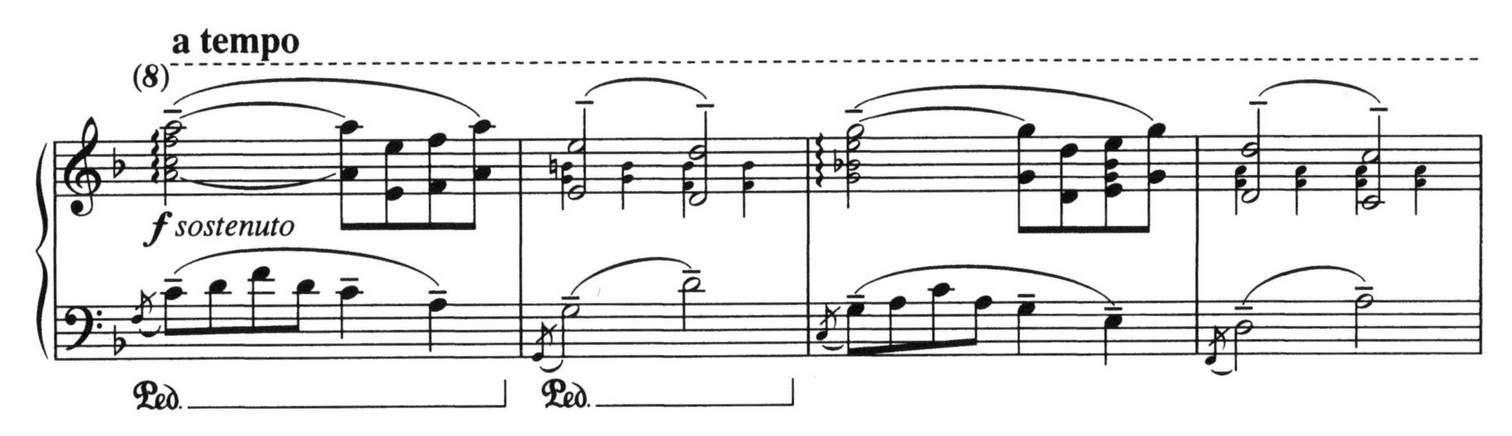
a tempo
(8)
f sostenuto
Ped.
Ped.

(8)
(8)
rall. e dim.
(8)
f
a tempo
pp
molto espress.
with soft pedal
rall.
molto rit. al fine
8va
pp
Ped.